NEVER TOO YOUNG

YOUNG

SPIRIT & SONG FOR YOUNG PEOPLE

*A Music Resource for
Prayer, Worship & Classroom*

OCP

spiritandsong.com®
a division of ocp

Never Too Young: Spirit & Song for Young People
© 2007, spiritandsong.com®, a division of OCP
5536 NE Hassalo, Portland, OR 97213
Phone: (503) 281-1191
E-mail address: liturgy@ocp.org
              support@spiritandsong.com
Web pages: ocp.org
            spiritandsong.com

John J. Limb, *Publisher*

Thomas N. Tomaszek, *Director, Artist Relations & Product Development*
Randall DeBruyn and Robert Feduccia, *Associate Directors, Artist Relations & Product Development*

Tom Booth, Mark Friedman, Janet Vogt, *Project Consultants*

Eric Schumock, *Director, Editorial Processes*
Joanne Osborn, *Executive Editor*; Amanda Weller, *Managing Editor/Project Editor*;
Angela Westhoff-Johnson, *Managing Editor*; Rick Modlin, *Managing Arranger*

Lisa Arakelian, *Primary Editor*; Ken Canedo, Estela García-López, C. Angelyn Jáuregui, Craig Kingsbury, Rodolfo López, Mark Nieves, Theresa Schumacher, William Schuster, David Simmons, Mary K. Straub, Alan Tarpinian, *Editing Assistance*

Steve Grundy, *Engraving Manager*
Laura C. Kantor, *Primary Engraver*; Victoria Baker, Mónica Germano, Scott Hall, Chris Luttrell, Sharon Norton, Jon Taubman, *Music Engraving*

Gus Torres, *Art Director*; Judy Urben, *Graphic Designer*

Leanna Nudo, *Contract Administration Manager*; Shirley McKenna, *Permissions Administrator*

Assembly Book	ISBN-13: 978-1-57992-139-2	edition 20344
Guitar Accompaniment Book	ISBN-13: 978-1-57992-140-8	edition 20345
Keyboard Accompaniment Book	ISBN-13: 978-1-57992-141-5	edition 20346
Compact Discs		
Vocal Edition		edition 20348
Instrumental Edition		edition 20349

Some titles available separately online.
Please visit http://www.ocp.org/en/print/single.php for more information.

Edition No. 20344
ISBN-13: 978-1-57992-139-2

CONTENTS

*These indexes may be found in the accompaniment books.
Complete indexes may be found online. Please visit ocp.org.

PREFACE

Welcome to *Never Too Young: Spirit & Song for Young People*, the latest resource for ministering with young people through contemporary Catholic music. In 1999, *Spirit & Song* debuted as a volume of both familiar and new songs dedicated to the faith development of youth and young adults. The second volume, *Spirit & Song 2*, released in 2005, provided additional songs rooted in our Church's tradition expressed through a contemporary sound. *Never Too Young: Spirit & Song for Young People* now offers music and prayer resources that have been uniquely selected and prepared for youth primarily in grades four through eight.

We are delighted to know that people across the generations are singing and praying with the first two volumes of *Spirit & Song* and with the supplemental resource, *Choose Christ*. We have designed *Never Too Young* specifically as a resource for children and youth, ages 8 through 13, who participate in catechetical programs and Catholic schools. Music can be a valuable tool in assisting young disciples as they engage the ancient and rich apostolic faith. *Never Too Young* is specifically crafted for them, their needs, and these settings.

We have selected familiar songs from *Spirit & Song*, *Spirit & Song 2*, and the *Rise Up and Sing* collections based on the pastoral needs of young people in middle school. Many songs included from the first wave of contemporary music have new arrangements. For example, the popular "Come to the Water" by John Foley has a new arrangement and additional lyrics. Some traditional hymns similarly have new arrangements. In addition to the familiar, there are new songs from *Spirit & Song* composers Steve Angrisano, Josh Blakesley, Tom Booth, Bob Halligan, Sarah Hart, ValLimar Jansen, Matt Maher, Jesse Manibusan and Curtis Stephan. We are delighted to include new music from Gerard Chiusano, Mark Friedman, Janet Vogt, Christopher Walker and other OCP composers who work with children. Most notably, Carey Landry, one of the pioneers in Catholic music for young people, contributed the title song, "Never Too Young."

Never Too Young is intended to be used wherever young people are gathered. The music is arranged in sections by its primary ritual or catechetical function: gathering/sending, psalms, communion, praise and worship, prayer and devotion, music for the school and church year, sacramental music, and music for Christian living. However, particular attention was given to the multilingual and multicultural needs of Catholic schools. We have addressed the unique rhythm of the school year with helpful indexes in planning for both prayer and education.

All of the music in *Never Too Young* is recorded and available in compact disc format. The recordings provide an audio reference for accompanists, instrumentalists, choirs, and song leaders wanting to learn or teach new material. These recordings are also intended for use in the classroom and catechetical settings, personal prayer, or for the pure enjoyment of good, uplifting music. In addition, as we have done for many of our children's recordings, there is a complete set of instrumental tracks without lead vocals.

Additional resources to those contained in *Never Too Young* are available online. We encourage pastoral leaders to use PrintandPraise.com, our print-on-demand resource site, for further assistance. Liturgy.com, our comprehensive liturgy-planning resource, will assist those who prepare prayer and liturgy on a regular or occasional basis. Song suggestions for the *Spirit & Song* repertoire as well as scriptural, homiletic, prayer and planning materials may be found there. New music and emerging artists, podcasts and video are available at spiritandsong.com. While there you can discover new songs, listen 24/7 to our radio stations, hear and read artist reflections, watch interviews with artists, check event listings and find links to other helpful resources.

We wish to thank all who helped form *Never Too Young*. In particular, we thank John Limb, OCP's publisher, who inspires us to provide the Church with greater music, deeper worship, and wholehearted service. Special thanks and recognition are offered to the music selection and design team: Angela Westhoff-Johnson, Rick Modlin, Tom Booth, Amanda Weller, Joanne Osborn, Mark Friedman and Janet Vogt; and Mark Nieves and Ken Canedo for their advisement. We are truly grateful to OCP's editorial staff for their tireless efforts: Lisa Arakelian, Angie Jáuregui, Theresa Schumacher, Estela García-López, Craig Kingsbury, Rodolfo López, Rick Modlin, Joanne Osborn, Amanda Weller, Angela Westhoff-Johnson and William Schuster; to Ed Bolduc, Janet Vogt, David Brinker and Lourdes Montgomery for their outstanding arrange-ments; Kevin Walsh, Rick Modlin, Tom Booth, Mark Friedman, Janet Vogt, Bob Halligan, Sarah Hart, Santiago Fernández, Janèt Sullivan Whitaker, Craig Colson, Tom Kendzia, Trevor Thomson, Mike Moore, Dean Baskerville, Jeff Thomas and Don Turney for their recordings and production leadership; Gus Torres and Judy Urben for the cover design; Steve Grundy, Mónica Germano, Scott Hall, Laura Kantor, Chris Luttrell, Jon Taubman and Sharon Norton for their music engraving; Leanna Nudo, Shirley McKenna and the contract administration staff; Regina Alilat, our administrative assistant, and many others who advised and added their expertise to the process.

It is quite an honor to work with the OCP family of artists, songwriters and lyricists who contributed their music to *Never Too Young*. Their talents, gifts, and ministry flow from a life conformed to Christ in the Holy Spirit and for the glory of God.

We pray for all who use this resource and sing these songs, that they may enjoy a vital and personal relationship with the living and true God.

Thomas N. Tomaszek
Director of Artists and Repertoire

Randall DeBruyn
Executive Editor English-Language Worship Publications

Robert Feduccia, Jr.
Manager of Spirit & Song

The Feast of the Immaculate Conception
December 8, 2006

1   All the Ends of the Earth

Bobby Fisher

Refrain: All

All the ends of the earth, sing a joy - ful song.

Sing to the Lord, there is sal - va - tion.

All the ends of the earth, sing a joy - ful song.

Sing to the Lord, there is sal - va - tion.

1-3 **2** to Verses | **Final**

Sing to the Lord, there is sal - va - tion.

Verse 1: Cantor

1. Sing a new song to the Lord, our God.

1. For he has worked won - ders near and far.

1. Our God's right hand and ho - ly arm

to Refrain

1. have brought sal - va - tion to the world.

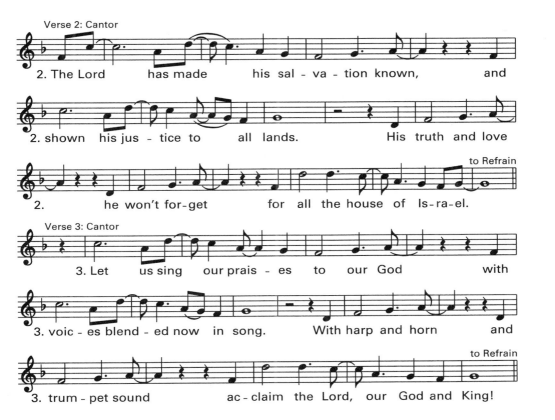

Verse 2: Cantor

2. The Lord has made his sal - va - tion known, and 2. shown his jus - tice to all lands. His truth and love 2. he won't for-get for all the house of Is-ra-el.

to Refrain

Verse 3: Cantor

3. Let us sing our prais - es to our God with 3. voic - es blend - ed now in song. With harp and horn and 3. trum - pet sound ac - claim the Lord, our God and King!

to Refrain

2

Alle, Alle, Alleluia

Fr. Richard Ho Lung

Refrain Al - le, al - le, al - le - lu - ia,
Verses 1. Fa - ther, Fa - ther, mak - er of the world.
        2. Je - sus, Je - sus, Je - sus is the way.
        3. Spir - it, Spir - it, come down on us, Lord.

        al - le, al - le, al - le - lu - ia.
1. Fa - ther, Fa - ther, cre - a - tor of the earth.
2. Je - sus, Je - sus, Je - sus is the truth.
3. Spir - it, Spir - it, rain down on us, Lord.

        Al - le, al - le, al - le - lu - ia.
1. Fa - ther, Fa - ther, speak - er of the word.
2. Je - sus, Je - sus, Je - sus is the life.
3. Spir - it, Spir - it, flood us with your pow'r.

        Al - le, al - le, al - le, al - le - lu - ia.
1. Make us, Fa - ther, break us, Fa - ther, mold us in your ways.
2. Je - sus is the way, he is the truth, he is the life.
3. Fill us with the light of God, oh, fill us with your pow'r.

[1-6]

        Al - le, al - le, al - le, al - le - lu - ia. (to Verses)
1. Make us, Fa - ther, break us, Fa - ther, mold us in your ways. (to Refrain)
2. Je - sus is the way, he is the truth, he is the life. (to Refrain)
3. Fill us with the light of God, oh, fill us with your pow'r. (to Refrain)

Final

ia. Al - le, al - le, al - le - lu - ia.

Al - le, al - le, al - le - lu - ia. Al - le!

Alleluia! Give the Glory

3

Ken Canedo

Refrain: All

Al-le-lu-ia!   Al-le-lu-ia!

Al-le-lu - ia!   Give the glo-ry

1. and the hon-or   to the Lord!

2. and the hon-or   to the Lord!   to Verses

*Verses: Cantor or All

1. Where two or three are gath-ered _____ in my
2. I am the vine and you _____ are the

1. name, _____ there I am in the
2. branch-es. _____ A - bide in _____

1. midst of them; _____ there I'll be. _____
2. me _____ and _____ bear much fruit. _____   to Refrain

Text: Based on Matthew 18:20; John 15:5; Ken Canedo and Bob Hurd. Text and music © 1991, Ken Canedo and Bob Hurd. Published by OCP. All rights reserved.

*Gospel verses available in accompaniment books.

4

Alleluia! Sing to Jesus

HYFRYDOL
Arranged by Cyprian Consiglio

1. Al - le - lu - ia! Sing to Je - sus! His the scep - ter,
2. Al - le - lu - ia! Not as or - phans are we left in
3. Al - le - lu - ia! King E - ter - nal, you the Lord of

1. his the throne. Al - le - lu - ia! His the tri - umph,
2. sor - row now; Al - le - lu - ia! He is near us,
3. lords we own. Al - le - lu - ia! Son of Ma - ry,

1. his the vic - to - ry a - lone; Hark! The songs
2. faith be - lieves, nor ques - tions how: Though the clouds
3. son of God from heav - en's throne. Our sal - va -

1. of peace - ful Zi - on thun - der like a
2. from sight re - ceived him when the for - ty
3. - tion you ac - com - plished, robed in flesh, our

1. might - y flood; Je - sus out of
2. days were o'er, shall our hearts for -
3. new High Priest; here on earth both

1. ev - 'ry na - tion has re-deemed us by his
2. get his prom - ise, "I am with you ev - er -
3. priest and vic - tim in the Eu - cha - ris - tic

1	2	Final
3 to Verse 2	6 to Verse 3	

1. blood.
2. more"?
3. feast.

Text: William Dix, 1837–1898, alt. Music: Based on HYFRYDOL; Rowland H. Prichard, 1811–1887.
Arrangement © 1988, Cyprian Consiglio, OSB Cam. Published by OCP. All rights reserved.

Christopher Walker

Refrain
At the name of Je-sus, ev-'ry knee shall bow, ev-'ry tongue con-
fess him: King of glo-ry now. (last time only) Je-sus is Lord, King of glo-ry now!

Verses
1. He ___ emp-tied him-self, as a slave, yet free,
2. He ___ hum-bled him-self, and o-beyed God's will.
3. God ex-alt - ed him, raised him up on high
4. Christ ___ Je-sus will come at the end of time,

1. came in hu - man like-ness___ for you and for me; in
2. On a cross he died_____ on Cal-va-ry's hill; for
3. so a-bove all oth-ers ___ his name will not die; that
4. come with ju - bi - la-tion ___ to call ___ us home. Un -

1. hu - man like-ness ___ for you and for me.
2. you and me he o-beyed ___ God's will.
3. name we hon - or _____ and glo - ri - fy.
4. til that day you and I will pro - claim:

to Refrain

Refrain text: Caroline Maria Noel, 1817–1877. Verses text: Based on Philippians 2.
Music and verses text © 1995, Christopher Walker. Published by OCP. All rights reserved.

6   Blessed Be Your Name

Matt and Beth Redman

Verses

1. Bless - ed be your name in the land that
   Bless - ed be your name when I'm found in
2. Bless - ed be your name when the sun's shin -
   Bless - ed be your name on the road marked

1. is plen - ti - ful, where your streams of a - bun -
   the des - ert place, though I walk through the wil -
2. ing down on me, when the world's all as it
   with suf - fer - ing, though there's pain in the of -

1. dance flow, bless - ed be your name.
   der - ness, bless - ed be your name.
2. should be, bless - ed be your name.
   fer - ing, bless - ed be your name.

1, 2. Ev-'ry bless-ing you pour out I'll turn back to praise.

1, 2. When the dark-ness clos-es in, Lord, still I will say,

Refrain

"Bless-ed be the name of the Lord! Bless-ed be your

name! Bless-ed be the name of the Lord!

1   to Verse 2   *2, 4*

Bless-ed be your glo - ri - ous name!"

Gathering/Sending

You give and take a - way! You
give and take a - way! My heart will choose to say,
"Lord, bless-ed be your name!" You give and take a -
way! You give and take a - way! My heart will choose to
say, "Lord, bless - ed be your name!"

Text: Based on Job 1:20–22; Habakkuk 3:17–18. Text and music © 2002, Thankyou Music (PRS). All rights reserved.
Administered by EMI CMG Publishing. Used with permission.

Gathering/Sending

7

Bless the Lord

Dan Brennan, Marc Cavallero,
Kevin Roth and Ken Canedo

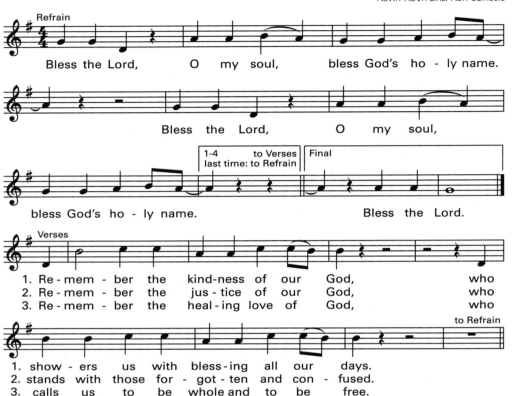

Refrain

Bless the Lord, O my soul, bless God's ho-ly name.

Bless the Lord, O my soul,

1-4 to Verses
last time: to Refrain

Final

bless God's ho-ly name. Bless the Lord.

Verses

1. Re-mem-ber the kind-ness of our God, who
2. Re-mem-ber the jus-tice of our God, who
3. Re-mem-ber the heal-ing love of God, who

to Refrain

1. show-ers us with bless-ing all our days.
2. stands with those for-got-ten and con-fused.
3. calls us to be whole and to be free.

Gathering/Sending

Christ, Be Our Light

Bernadette Farrell

Verses

1. Long-ing for light, __ we wait in dark-ness. Long-ing for
2. Long-ing for peace, __ our world is trou-bled. Long-ing for
3. Long-ing for food, __ man-y are hun-gry. Long-ing for
4. Long-ing for shel-ter, man-y are home-less. Long-ing for
5. Man-y the gifts, __ man-y the peo-ple, man-y the

1. truth, _____ we turn to you. Make us your own, _____
2. hope, _____ man-y de-spair. Your word a-lone _____
3. wa-ter, man-y still thirst. Make us your bread, ____
4. warmth, __ man-y are cold. Make us your build-ing,
5. hearts that yearn to be-long. Let us be ser-vants

1. your ho-ly peo-ple, light for the world to see.
2. has pow'r to save us. Make us your liv-ing voice.
3. bro-ken for oth-ers, shared un-til all are fed.
4. shel-ter-ing oth-ers, walls made of liv-ing stone.
5. to one an-oth-er, mak-ing your king-dom come.

Refrain

Christ, be our light! Shine in our hearts. Shine through the dark-ness.

Christ, be our light! Shine in your church gath-ered to-day.

9

City of God

Dan Schutte

Verses 1, 2

1. A-wake from your slum-ber! A - rise from your
2. We are sons of the morn-ing; we are daugh-ters of

1. sleep! A new day is dawn-ing for all those who weep.
2. day. The One who has loved us has bright-ened our way.

1. The peo - ple in dark-ness have seen a great light. The
2. The Lord of all kind-ness has called us to be a

to Refrain

1. Lord of our long-ing has con-quered the night.
2. light for his peo-ple to set their hearts free.

Refrain

Let us build the cit-y of God. May our tears be

turned in - to danc - ing! For the Lord, our light and our

love, has turned the night in - to day!

Verse 3

3. God is light; in him there is no dark-ness.

3. Let us walk in his light, his chil - dren,

3. one and all. O com-fort my

3. peo-ple; make gen-tle your words. Pro-claim to my

3. cit-y ... the day of her birth.

Verse 4

4. O cit-y of glad-ness, now lift up your voice!

to Refrain

4. Pro-claim the good tid-ings that all may re - joice!

Text: Based on Isaiah 9; 40:1–9; 1 John 1. Text and music © 1981, Daniel L. Schutte and OCP. All rights reserved.

Gather Your People

10

Bob Hurd

Refrain

Gath-er your peo-ple, O Lord. Gath-er your peo-ple, O Lord. One bread, one bod-y, one spir-it of love. Gath-er your peo-ple, O Lord.

Verses

1. Draw us forth to the ta - ble of life:
2. We are parts of the bod - y of Christ,
3. No more harm on the moun-tain of God;
4. Wash us, Lord, in the wa - ters of life;

1. broth - ers and sis - ters, each of us called to
2. need - ing each oth - er, each of the gifts the
3. swords in - to plow-shares. Free us, O Lord, from
4. wa - ters of mer - cy, wa - ters of hope that

to Refrain

1. walk in your light.
2. Spir - it pro - vides.
3. hard - ness of heart.
4. flow from your side.

Text: Based on 1 Corinthians 12; Isaiah 2:3–4, 11:9. Text and music © 1991, Bob Hurd. Published by OCP. All rights reserved.

Give God the Glory

Sarah Hart

Verses

1. Great and won-der-ful is the God of A - bra-ham.
2. Wise and mer - ci - ful is the God of Pe - ter.

1. Great and won - der-ful is the God of Sa - rah.
2. Wise and mer - ci - ful is the God of Ma - ry.

1. Great and won-der-ful is the God of ev - 'ry - one,
2. Wise and mer - ci - ful is the God of ev - 'ry-thing.

1. the great I AM, the one who made us all.
2. Je - sus, the one who came to set us free.

Refrain

We're gon - na give God the glo - ry; we're gon - na give

God the praise. We're gon - na give God the glo - ry; we're

1, Final   *Interlude*   **4** *to Verse 2*

gon - na love him all our days.

2   *to Refrain*   *3*   **A** *Bridge* / Voice 1

our days.   our days.   Oh, sing al - le-lu - ia.

Oh, sing al - le-lu - ia. Oh, sing

al - le - lu - ia.   Oh,   sing   al - le - lu - ia.

B Sing 1 time
C Sing 2 times
(Voice 1)

Oh,   sing   al - le - lu - ia.   Oh,   sing

Voice 2

We're gon - na give   God   the glo - ry;   we're gon - na give

al - le - lu - ia.   Oh,   sing   al - le -

God   the praise.   We're gon - na give   God   the

lu - ia.   Oh,   sing   al - le - lu - ia.

glo - ry; we're   gon - na love him   all   our   days.

7   to Refrain

12 Go Ye Out

Tom Booth

Refrain

Go ye out and tell all the na-tions, tell all the na-

-tions of his love! Go ye out and

tell all the na-tions, *1, 2* tell all the na-tions of his love! *to Verses*

3 tell all the na-tions of his love! *to Bridge*

4, Final tell all the na-tions of his love! *to Refrain (Fine)*

Verse 1

1. Praise ye the Lord! Praise him, all you na-tions! Glo-ri-fy him,

1. all you peo-ples! Praise ye the Lord! You got to

1. praise him, all you na-tions! Glo-ri-fy him, all you peo-ples! *to Refrain 2*

Verse 2

2. Stead-fast is his love, his kind-ness lasts for-ev-er. his

2. love is pure, last-ing all our days! Stead-fast is his love,

2. his kind-ness lasts for-ev-er. His

to Refrain

2. love is pure, last-ing all our days!

Bridge (sing 3 times)

*Kwen-da mwam-bi-a dun-i-a ma-zim-a! Kwen-da

mwam-bi-a dun-i-a ma-zim-a!

(spoken)

**A-llez di-re à toutes les na-tions!

Kwen-da mwam-bi-a dun-i-a ma-zim-a!

to Refrain

A-llez di-re à toutes les na-tions!

to Refrain

Kwen-da mwam-bi-a dun-i-a ma-zim-a! Go ye out!

*KiSwahili: Go and tell the whole world!
**French: Go, tell all the nations!

13

Glory Bound

Christopher Walker

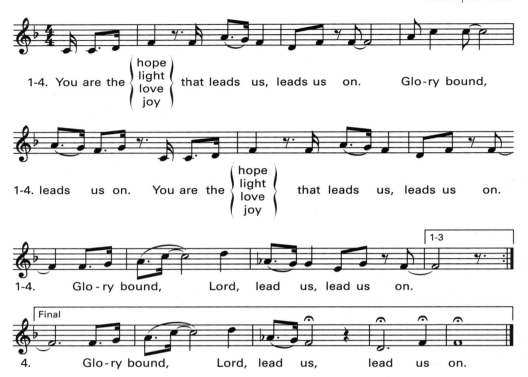

1-4. You are the { hope light love joy } that leads us, leads us on.   Glo-ry bound,

1-4. leads   us on.   You are the { hope light love joy } that leads   us, leads us   on.

1-3

1-4.   Glo-ry bound,   Lord,   lead   us, lead us   on.

Final

4.   Glo-ry bound,   Lord,   lead   us,   lead   us   on.

Text: Paule Freeburg, DC. Text and music © 2006, Paule Freeburg, DC and Christopher Walker. Published by OCP. All rights reserved.

Gathering/Sending

God, Creator, God Most High

14

Janet Vogt

Refrain

God, Cre-a-tor, God Most High, be our ev-er pres-ent light. Be a-mong us, here be-fore us, God with-in us.

Verses

1. You are light for the world. You are light for the lost to see.
2. You re-stored night to day. You com-mand-ed the dark to cease.
3. You are God for all time, source of all of our hope and faith.

1. Out of dark-ness we come to the light of your love, for your word is a lamp un-to our feet to guide us.
2. By your prom-ise of love we shall not walk in fear. We shall walk in the light of hope and peace to guide us.
3. Call your peo-ple a-gain to go forth and re-new all the earth with the strength of love and grace to guide us.

to Refrain

*Last time: Repeat final phrase.

15 Holy, Holy, Holy

Timothy R. Smith

1. Ho-ly, Ho-ly, Ho-ly! Lord ___ God Al-might-y! Early in the morning our song shall rise to thee: Ho-ly, Ho-ly, Ho-ly! Merciful and mighty, God in three Persons, blessed Trinity.

2. Ho-ly, Ho-ly, Ho-ly! All the saints adore thee, Casting down their golden crowns around the glassy sea; Cher-u-bim and seraphim falling down before thee, Who was, and is, and evermore shall be.

3. Ho-ly, Ho-ly, Ho-ly! Though the darkness hide thee, Though the eye of sinners thy glory may not see, Only thou art holy; there is none beside thee, Perfect in Pow'r, in love, and purity.

4. Ho-ly, Ho-ly, Ho-ly! Lord ___ God Al-might-y! All thy works shall praise thy Name in earth and sky and sea; Ho-ly, Ho-ly, Ho-ly! Merciful and mighty, God in three Persons, blessed Trinity!

1, Final — to Verse 2 | 2, 3 | 4 — to Verses 3, 4

1. ty. 2. be.
4. ty! 3. ty.

Text: Reginald Heber, 1783–1826. Music © 1999, Timothy R. Smith. Published by spiritandsong.com®, a division of OCP. All rights reserved.

In This Holy Place

16

Mark Friedman and Janet Vogt

Verses

1. Gath - er to-geth - er the rich and the poor.
2. Chil - dren of God, to this ta - ble we come.
3. From ev - 'ry cor - ner of earth now pro - claim:

1. Wel - come the old and the young to our door.
2. Though we are man - y, we gath - er as one.
3. we are a fam - 'ly in Christ's ho - ly name.

1. Shep-herd the faith - ful, the lost and for - lorn,
2. Called by the Spir - it, our hearts turn to you:
3. Sing al - le - lu - ia with hearts filled with praise,

1. here in the bod - y of Christ now re - born.
2. God of cre - a - tion, the world is made new.
3. build - ing the king - dom of love all our days.

Refrain

In this ho - ly place, we will know God's lov-ing em -

brace, one in the Spir - it and filled with God's grace,

1, 2, Final

in this ho - ly place.

to Verses 2, 3 | *3*

4

to Refrain

place.

Jesus Christ, You Are My Life

Marco Frisina

Refrain

English	Je - sus Christ,____	you are my life,	al - le - lu -
Spanish	Je - su - cris - to,	vi - ves en mí,	a - le - lu -
French	Jé - sus - Christ,____	tu es ma vie,	al - lé - lu -
Italian	Cris - to vi - ve	in mez-zo a noi,	al - le - lu -
Vietnamese	Giê - su Ki - tô,	Chuá ở cùng con,	al - le - lu -

- ia, al - le - lu - ia.	Je - sus Christ,____
- ya, a - le - lu - ya.	Je - su - cris - to,
- ia, al - lé - lu - ia.	Jé - sus - Christ,____
- ia, al - le - lu - ia.	Cris - to vi - ve
- ia, al - le - lu - ia.	Giê - su Ki - tô,

to Verses

you are my life.	You are my life,	al - le - lu - ia.
vi - ves en mí,	vi - ves en mí,	a - le - lu - ya.
tu es ma vie,	tu es ma vie,	al - lé - lu - ia.
in mez-zo a noi,	in mez-zo a noi,	al - le - lu - ia.
Chuá trong tâm hồn,	Chuá trong tâm hồn,	al - le - lu - ia.

Last time

You are my life,	al - le - lu - ia.
Vi - ves en mí,	a - le - lu - ya.
Tu es ma vie,	al - lé - lu - ia.
In mez-zo a noi,	al - le - lu - ia.
Chuá trong tâm hồn,	al - le - lu - ia.

Verses

English	1. Be our Way, our Truth, and our Life.
	2. Ho - ly fire, come dwell in each heart.
	3. Break the yoke of vio - lence and war.
	4. Sense - less walls of ha - tred di - vide,
Spanish	5. Que la I - gle - sia se - a tu voz,
	6. Cuan - do su - fro per - se - cu - ción
	7. Si hay o - dio y hay o - pre - sión,
	8. Cum - ple tu pro - me - sa, Se - ñor,
	9. Tú me un - ges pa - ra lle - var
	10. Con tu guí - a dé - ja - me ser
French	11. Tu nous ras - sembles dans l'u - ni - té.
Italian	12. Tu sei vi - a, sei ve - ri - tà,
Vietnamese	13. Tình Ngài diu êm như mạch suối mát
	14. Ngài là lửa thiêng soi dời tăm tối
	15. Ngài là bài ca cho dời con hát

Gathering/Sending

1. Form us a - new in___ how you died. We em - brace the
2. Grant us the gifts your__ love im - parts. Free our tongues to
3. O - pen the hearts of__ rich to poor. Na - tions bound by
4. __ven-geance de - stroys and__ fear mis-guides. Teach us mer - cy:
5. un sa - cra - men - to de san - ti - dad. Da - nos fuer - za
6. por pro - cla - mar tu__ nom - bre, ha - llo fuer - za al
7. __haz que tu ros - tro__ bri - lle en mí; que mis ac - tos
8. llé - na - me con tu Es - pí - ri - tu; que mi vi - da a -
9. la bue - na nue - va a los po - bres y a - nun - ciar su
10. __un ins - tru - men - to__ de tu a - mor; con tu gra - cia a -
11. Re - un - is dans ton__ grand a - mour. De - vant toi__
12. tu sei la nos - tra__ vi - ta, cam - mi - nan - do
13. Bước đi bên Ngài hạnh__ phúc miên man. Chúa chính là nguồn
14. Thắp sáng yêu thương tình__ Chúa cao vời Chúa hỡi tình Ngài
15. Hát cho muôn người cùng__ khắp muôn nơi. Có Chúa cuộc đời

to Refrain

1. cross that you bore, and will a - rise in glo - ry.
2. bold - ly pro-claim "Je - sus is Lord for - ev - er!"
3. ter - ror and fear long to em - brace your free - dom.
4. __hope for new life; for you a - lone are ho - ly!
5. pa - ra lo - grar e - di - fi - car tu Rei - no.
6. ir con mi cruz jun - to a ti, O Cris - to.
7. __mues-tren tu paz y tu jus - ti - cia al mun - do.
8. yu - de a tra - er tu e - van - ge - lio al mun - do.
9. li - be - ra - ción a los que es-tán cau - ti - vos.
10. __yú - da - me hoy a pro - cla - mar tus o - bras.
11. dans la__ joie nous chan - ter - ons ta gloire.__
12. __in - sie-me a te viv - rem o in te per sem - pre.
13. bình an vô giá Để con náu thân Chúa hải hà.
14. dìu con đi tới Để yêu Chúa thôi mãi trọn đời.
15. từ nay đổi mới Cùng vang tiếng ca Chúa thương ta.

Text: English refrain, Italian and French refrain and verses, Marco Frisina; Spanish refrain and English verses, Rufino Zaragoza, OFM; Spanish verses, Jaime Cortez; Vietnamese, Xuan Minh. Text and music © 2000, 2004, Laus Edizioni Musicali S.R.J. and Multimedia San Paulo. All rights reserved. Exclusive agent for English-language countries: OCP.

Gathering/Sending

18   In This Place

Trevor Thomson

Verses

1. We are all hun-gry peo - ple, we need shel - ter and
2. All our lives are a Mys-t'ry; we see not where they
3. Though the world may __ tell us to __ look at our -
4. In the bread that is bro - ken is the Christ that re -

1. strength. We are one in our hurt - ing, we are
2. lead. We are asked now to trust you and we
3. selves, we reach out to an - oth - er where
4. stores. As we take, now re - ceive him, we find

1. one ___ in our pain. In our suf - f'ring and sad - ness,
2. know we must be - lieve. As our feet be - come Christ's feet,
3. suf - fer - ing dwells. As our hands be - come Christ's hands,
4. love ___ ev - er - more. As the bread be - comes Bod - y,

1. we are saved by the grace
2. we go forth with the grace   of the pow - er and the
3. we are healed by the grace
4. we are filled with the grace

Refrain

1-4. Spir - it that is here in this place.   We are

gath - ered at ta - ble as ___ one in the Lord.   We are
(*to - geth - er)
gath - ered as peo - ple who are liv - ing the Word.   Our ___

hearts and our spir - its are nur - tured by grace.   It is

Je - sus who fills us. He is here in this place.

*Alternative text.

Lead Me, Lord

John D. Becker

Verses

1. Bless - ed are the poor in spir - it, long - ing for their
2. Bless - ed are the mer - ci - ful, for mer - cy shall be
3. Blest are they who through their life - times sow the seeds of

1. Lord, for God's com - ing king - dom shall be theirs.
2. theirs, and the pure in heart shall see their God.
3. peace, all will call them chil - dren of the Lord.

1. Bless - ed are the sor - row - ing, for they shall be con -
2. Blest are they whose hun - ger on - ly ho - li - ness can
3. Blest are you, though per - se - cu - ted in your ho - ly

1. soled, and the meek shall come to rule the world.
2. fill, for I say they shall be sat - is - fied.
3. life, for in heav - en, great is your re - ward.

Refrain

Lead me, Lord, lead me, Lord, by the light of truth to

seek and to find the nar - row way. Be my way;

be my truth; be my life, my Lord, and lead me, Lord, to -

1-2 to Verses **Final**

day.   day.   And lead me, Lord, to - day.

Text: Matthew 5:3–12; 7:7, 13; John 14:6. Text and music © 1987, John D. Becker. Published by OCP. All rights reserved.

Lead Us to the Water: Gathering

Tom Kendzia and Gary Daigle

Let the River Flow

Darrell Evans

Verse

Let the poor man say, "I am rich in him."
Let the blind man say, "I can see a-gain."

Let the lost man say, "I am found in him."
Let the dead man say, "I am born a-gain."

Oh, let the riv - er flow.

Oh, let the riv - er flow.

Refrain

Let the riv-er flow. Let the riv-er flow.

Ho - ly Spir-it, come; move in pow - er. Let the

sing 3 times

riv - er flow. (Let the riv - er flow.) Let the

riv - er flow.

22   Let Us Come to Be One Body

Jaime Cortez

Refrain

Let us come to be one bod - y as we glo - ri - fy our God and re - call the pas - chal mys - ter - y of Christ. Let the pow - er of the Ho - ly Spir - it sanc - ti - fy our lives, and re - store all cre - a - tion, bring - ing clos - er ev - 'ry na - tion; let this be the cel - e - bra - tion that brings hope in - to the world.

Verses

1. East to west sa - cred sto - ries which are spo - ken
2. Hand in hand with our sis - ters and our broth - ers,
3. One by one ev - 'ry per - son will be count - ed,

1. and the bread that's blest and bro - ken bring hu -
2. we bring heal - ing to each oth - er so the
3. no re - quest shall be dis - count - ed, and the

1. man - i - ty to har - mo - ny with God.
2. reign of God can shine with - in our world.
3. vic - to - ry of jus - tice will pre - vail.

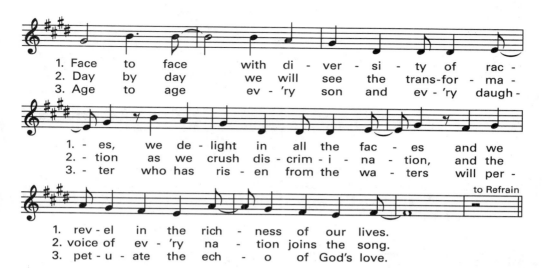

1. Face to face with di-ver-si-ty of rac-
2. Day by day we will see the trans-for-ma-
3. Age to age ev-'ry son and ev-'ry daugh-

1. -es, we de-light in all the fac-es and we
2. -tion as we crush dis-crim-i-na-tion, and the
3. -ter who has ris-en from the wa-ters will per-

to Refrain

1. rev-el in the rich-ness of our lives.
2. voice of ev-'ry na-tion joins the song.
3. pet-u-ate the ech-o of God's love.

Lift Up Your Hearts

23

Roc O'Connor, SJ

Refrain

Lift up your hearts to the Lord, praise God's gra-cious mer-cy!

Sing out your joy to the Lord, whose love is en-dur-ing.

Verses

1. Shout with joy to the Lord, all the earth!
2. Let the earth wor-ship, sing-ing your praise.
3. God's right hand made a path through the night,
4. Lis-ten now, all you ser-vants of God,

1. Praise the name a-bove all names! Say to God, "How
2. Praise the glo-ry of your name! Come and see the
3. split the wa-ters of the sea. All cre-a-tion,
4. as I tell of these great works. Bless-ed be the

to Refrain

1. won-drous your works, how glo-rious your name!"
2. deeds of the Lord; bless God's ho-ly name!
3. lift up your voice: "Our God set us free!"
4. Lord of my life, whose love shall en-dure!

Gathering/Sending

24 Lord, Let Your Face Shine upon Us

Tom Booth

Refrain

Lord, let your face shine up-on us. Lord, let it shine.

Lord, let your face shine up-on us.

1, 5 to Refrain | 2-4 to Verses | Final

Lord, let it shine.

Verse 1

1. When I call, an - swer me, O my just God,

1. you who re - lieve me when I am in dis - tress; have

to Refrain

1. pit - y on me, and hear my prayer!

Verse 2

2. Know that the LORD does won - ders for his faith - ful one;

2. the LORD will hear me when I call up - on him. LORD, let the

to Refrain

2. light of your face shine up - on us!

Verse 3

3. You put glad - ness in - to my heart.

3. As I lie down, I fall peace-ful a-sleep. You a-

to Refrain

3. lone, O LORD, bring peace to my home.

Rain Down

25

Jaime Cortez

Refrain

Rain down, rain down, rain down your

1.

love on your peo - ple.

2.

love, God of life.

Verses

1. Faith-ful and true is the word of our God. All of God's
2. We who re - vere and find hope in our God live in the
3. God of cre - a - tion, we long for your truth; you are the

1. works are so wor-thy of trust. God's mer-cy falls on the
2. kind-ness and joy of God's wing. God will pro - tect us from
3. wa - ter of life that we thirst. Grant that your love and your

to Refrain

1. just and the right; full of God's love is the earth.
2. dark - ness and death; God will not leave us to starve.
3. peace touch our hearts, all of our hope lies in you.

Malo! Malo! Thanks Be to God

Jesse Manibusan

Refrain: Cantor intones each phrase; All repeat

Ma - lo! Ma - lo! Thanks be to God!

O - bri - ga - do! Al - le - lu - ia!

¡Gra - ci - as! Kam sa ham ni da!

Ma - lo! Ma - lo! Thanks be to God! (to Verses)

Last time / repeat ad. lib. / Fine

Ma - lo! Ma - lo! Thanks be to God!

Verse 1: Cantor intones each phrase; All repeat

1. Si Yu - 'us ma - a' - se!

1. Teri - ma ka - sih! Ma - ra - ming

1. sa - la - mat! Dan - ke schön! Dzię -

1. ku - ję! We thank you, Lord! (to Refrain)

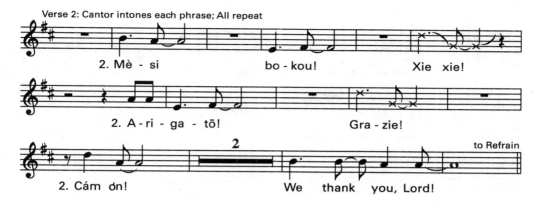

Verse 2: Cantor intones each phrase; All repeat

2. Mè - si   bo - kou!   Xie xie!

2. A - ri - ga - tō!   Gra - zie!

2. Cám ơn!   We   thank   you, Lord!

Pronunciation Guide

Refrain
Tongan   Malo Malo   **mah-loh mah-loh**
Portuguese   Obrigado   **o-bree-ga-doh**
Spanish   Gracias   **grah-seeahs**
Korean   Kam sa ham ni da   **kahm sah hahm nee dah**

Verse 1
Chamoru   Si Yu'us maa'se   **see joos mah-ah-sih**
Indonesian   Terima kasih   **three-mah kah-seeh**
Tagalog   Maraming salamat   **mah-rah-meeng sah-lah-maht**
German   Danke schön   **dahn-kuh shuh(r)n**
Polish   Dziękuję   **jehn-koo-yeh**

Verse 2
Creole   Mèsi bokou   **meh-see boh-koo**
Mandarin   Xie xie   **shee-eh shee-eh**
Japanese   Arigatō   **ah-ree-gah-toh**
Italian   Grazie   **grah-tsee-eh**
Vietnamese   Cám ơn   **gahm urn**

27 On Eagle's Wings

Michael Joncas

Verse 1

1. You who dwell in the shel-ter of the Lord, who a-bide in his

1. shad-ow for life, say to the Lord: "My ref-uge, my rock in whom I trust!"

Refrain

And he will raise you up on ea-gle's wings, bear you on the

breath of dawn, make you to shine like the

to Verses (last time to Coda)

sun, and hold you in the palm of his hand.

Coda

And hold you, hold you in the palm of his hand.

Verse 2

2. The snare of the fowl-er will nev-er cap-ture you, and fam-ine will bring

2. you no fear: un-der his wings your ref-uge, his faith-ful-ness your shield.

Verse 3

3. You need not fear the ter-ror of the night, nor the ar-row that flies by

3. day; though thou-sands fall a-bout you, near you it shall not come.

Verse 4

4. For to his an-gels he's giv-en a com-mand to

4. guard you in all of your ways; up-on their hands they will

to Refrain

4. bear you up, lest you dash your foot a-gainst a stone.

Sing Alleluia

28

Janet Vogt

Refrain

Sing al-le-lu - ia, sing. Sing al-le-lu - ia, sing.

Repeat 1st time

Sing al-le-lu - ia, sing, sing al-le-lu-ia to the Lord!

Verses

1. Joy - ful - ly we come this day
2. Praise God for all to hear and see,
3. A new com - mand - ment we will trust:
4. For - ev - er, God, your word shall be

1. in the pres-ence of God's grace. With God's love we sing
2. gath-ered as one fam - i - ly. Shine your light, re-joice
3. love as on - ly God loves us; so shall we love one
4. gift of hope for all who seek. God our ref-uge, God

to Refrain

1. as one, _____ al-le-lu - ia to the Lord!
2. and sing _____ al-le-lu - ia to the Lord!
3. an-oth - er, al-le-lu - ia to the Lord!
4. our strength, _____ al-le-lu - ia to the Lord!

Gathering/Sending

Our God Is Here

Chris Muglia

Verses

1. Here in this time, here in this place,
2. Here in the Word, God is re-vealed,

1. here we are stand - ing face to face. Here in our hearts,
2. here where the wound - ed can be healed. Here in our hearts,

1. here in our lives, our God is here.
2. here in our lives, our God is here.

1. Here for the bro - ken, here for the strong,
2. Here we be-come_____ what we re - ceive,

1. here in this tem - ple we be - long. Here in our hearts,_
2. here in this Eu - cha - ris - tic feast. We are his bod -

1. _____ here in our lives, our God is here.
2. - y, liv - ing as one; our God is here.

Refrain

And we cry: "Ho - ly! Ho - ly! Ho - ly are

you!" We cry: "Ho - ly! Ho - ly! Ho - ly and

true!" A - men, we do be-lieve our God is here.

1, 2

2

1: to Verse 2
2: to Bridge

Our God is here.

Gathering/Sending

Final A - men, we do be-lieve our God is here. Our God is here.

Bridge Our God is here. Our God is here. And we cry: *to Refrain*

30 O Love of God/Amor de Dios

Bob Hurd

Refrain

O love of God, gath-er us, a - mor de
Dios, haz-nos u - no, *that we may share the
gifts we are giv-en; **pa - ra cons-tru - ir
la co - mu - ni - dad, pa - ra cons-tru -
ir la co - mu - ni - dad. _____

Verses

1. En el a-gua de vi-da nos con-ver -
___ In the liv - ing wa-ter we have be -
2. Hay di - ver - sos do - nes, pe - ro un
___ Man - y gifts of the Spir - it, but the same
3. Haz-nos u - na fa - mi - lia que ___ se
Make us all ___ one fam - 'ly; bring us to -

to Refrain

1. ti - mos en cuer - po del Se - ñor. _____
___ come ___ one bod - y in the Lord. _____
2. só - lo Dios que nos ins - pi - ra. _____
___ God ___ who works them in us all. _____
3. u - ne por o - bras de tu a - mor. _____
geth - er to do the works of love. _____

Text: Based on 1 Corinthians 12:4–6, 12–13; Bob Hurd, Pia Moriarty, Ana Victoria Demezas and Jaime Cortez.
Text and music © 1994, Bob Hurd and Pia Moriarty. Published by OCP. All rights reserved.

*"para que compartamos los dones que hemos recibido"
**"for the upbuilding of the community"

Gathering/Sending

Somos el Cuerpo de Cristo/
We Are the Body of Christ

31

Jaime Cortez

Refrain: All

So-mos el cuer-po de Cris-to. We are the bod-y of
So-mos el cuer-po de Cris-to. We are the bod-y of

Christ. Y He-mos o - í - do_el lla - ma-do; we've an-swered
Christ. Tra - e - mos su san-to men-sa - je. We come to

1
2
to Verses
Cantor
Final

"Yes," to the call of the Lord.
bring the good news to the world. 3. Que world.

Verses
Cantor

1. Dios vie-ne_al mun-do_a tra - vés de no-so-tros.
   mun-do_a cum-plir la mi-sión de la I-gle-sia,
2. Ca - da per-so-na es par-te del rei-no;
   To - das las ra-zas que ha-bi-tan la tie-rra,   So-mos el cuer-po de
3. nues-tras ac-cio-nes re - fle-jen jus-ti - cia;
   Va - mos al mun-do_a cui - dar su re-ba - ño.

Cantor

1-3. Cris-to.
1. God is re-vealed when we love one an-oth-er.
   Bring-ing the light of God's mer-cy to oth-ers,
2. Put-ting a stop to all dis-crim-i-na-tion,
   All are in-vit-ed to feast in the ban-quet.
3. Stop-ping a-buse and re-liev-ing the hun-gry,
   Serv-ing each oth-er we build up the king-dom;

All
1
Cantor
2
to Refrain

1-3. We are the bod-y of Christ.
1. Al
2. ♩ Christ.
3. ♩

Tell It Out

Timothy R. Smith

Refrain

Tell it out, tell it loud, let the word be spread. Je-sus rose to save our souls, he's ris-en from the dead. Tell it out, tell it loud, let the word be spread. Je-sus rose to save our souls, he's ris-en from the dead.

Verse 1

1. There's no mis-un - der-stand-ing, it's sim-ple and it's true.
1. God sent us his on - ly Son, he died for you. With-
1. out him we are strang-ers, or-phans all a - lone. A-

to Refrain

1. dopt-ed by his sac - ri-fice, we have a home.

Verse 2

2. Faith finds a way of know - ing, feels a touch with-out a hand.
2. And the seed he's sow - ing guides our foot-prints in the sand.
2. But faith a - lone won't sat - is - fy the

2. hun - ger and the call: Feed the hun - gry,

2. heal the sick,— some-bod-y help me, when I fall.

Bridge 5

There's no mis-un - der-stand-ing, it's sim-ple and it's

to Refrain

true. God sent us his on-ly Son, he died for you.

The King of Love My Shepherd Is

33

ST. COLUMBA

1. The King of love my shep - herd is, Whose
2. Where streams of liv - ing wa - ter flow With
3. Per - verse and fool - ish I have strayed, But
4. In death's dark vale I fear no ill With
5. You spread a ta - ble in my sight, Your
6. And so through all the length of days Your

1. good - ness fails me nev - er; I noth - ing lack if
2. gen - tle care he leads me, And where the ver - dant
3. yet in love he sought me, And on his shoul - der
4. you, dear Lord, be - side me; Your rod and staff my
5. sav - ing grace be - stow - ing; And O what joy and
6. good - ness fails me nev - er: Good Shep - herd, may I

1. I am his, And he is mine for - ev - er.
2. pas - tures grow, With heav'n - ly food he feeds me.
3. gent - ly laid, And home, re - joic - ing, brought me.
4. com - fort still, Your cross be - fore to guide me.
5. true de - light From your pure chal - ice flow - ing!
6. sing your praise With - in your house for - ev - er.

Text: 87 87; based on Psalm 23; Matthew 18; John 10; Henry Williams Baker, 1821–1877, alt. Music: Trad. Irish Melody.

34   Venimos/We Come

Mark Friedman

Refrain

Cantor: ¡Ve-ni - mos,
All: we come!
Cantor: ¡Can-ta - mos,
All: we sing!

Cantor: ¡Ser-vi - mos,
All: we serve you!
Cantor: ¡Te que-re - mos, Dios!

1-4
1: to Refrain
2-4: to Vss

Final

All: We love you, O God!
All: ¡Te que-re - mos, Dios!

Verses

Cantor:
1. Ev - 'ry na - tion on earth will be one great peo - ple;
2. As we gath - er this day may we sing God's prais - es
3. All your chil - dren will sing of your ten - der mer - cy;

All:
1. for - ev - er peace will rule the land!
2. with ev - 'ry crea - ture on the earth!
3. may love be ev - er in our hearts!

to Refrain

35   We Are the Light of the World

Jean Anthony Greif
Arranged by Tom Tomaszek

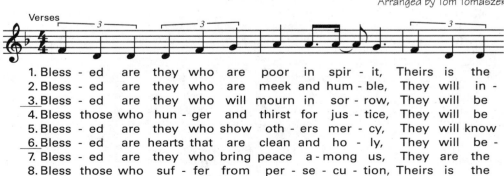

Verses

1. Bless - ed are they who are poor in spir - it, Theirs is the
2. Bless - ed are they who are meek and hum - ble, They will in -
3. Bless - ed are they who will mourn in sor - row, They will be
4. Bless those who hun - ger and thirst for jus - tice, They will be
5. Bless - ed are they who show oth - ers mer - cy, They will know
6. Bless - ed are hearts that are clean and ho - ly, They will be -
7. Bless - ed are they who bring peace a - mong us, They are the
8. Bless those who suf - fer from per - se - cu - tion, Theirs is the

1. king - dom of God.   Bless us, O Lord, make us
2. her - it the earth.   Bless us, O Lord, make us
3. com - fort - ed.   Bless us, O Lord, when we
4. sat - is - fied.   Bless us, O Lord, hear our
5. mer - cy too.   Bless us, O Lord, hear our
6. hold___ the Lord.   Bless us, O Lord, make us
7. chil - dren of God.   Bless us, O Lord, may your
8. king - dom of God.   Bless us, O Lord, when they

1. poor in spir - it;   Bless us, O Lord, our God.
2. meek and hum - ble;   Bless us, O Lord, our God.
3. share their sor - row;   Bless us, O Lord, our God.
4. cry for jus - tice;   Bless us, O Lord, our God.
5. cry for mer - cy;   Bless us, O Lord, our God.
6. pure and ho - ly;   Bless us, O Lord, our God.
7. peace be with us;   Bless us, O Lord, our God.
8. per - se - cute us;   Bless us, O Lord, our God.

Refrain

We are the light of the world, may our light shine be - fore

all, that they may see the good that we do, and give

1-7
glo - ry to God.

Final
God, and give

glo - ry to God, and give glo - ry to God.

36 We Gotta Love

Tom Booth, Israel Houghton and Matt Maher

Refrain

We got-ta love, love, love each oth-er.

We got-ta love, love, love our-selves.

And if we love, love, love with the love of the Lord,

we're giv-en all the hap-pi-ness that we could look for.

1, Final

2-4 to Verses/Bridge | **Verse 1**

1. I was lone-ly and a-fraid,

1. and with my eyes on me, I bare-ly

1. made it through the day. And then you

1. came to me with your un-end-ing love,

to Refrain

1. and now I want to shout it out: "There's hope from a-bove!"

Verse 2

2. Je - sus help me die to self, for in

2. giv - ing love is when we re - ceive. When my

2. heart is sad and I see no re - lief, you give me love

2. and you give me strength to love and be free.

Bridge

Love one an - oth - er, sis - ter and broth -

- er, fath - er and moth - er. Je - sus said,

to Refrain

"Love one an - oth - er, (love one an - oth - er) as I loved you!"

37

We Are Marching/Siyahamba

South African

We are march - ing in the light of God, we are
Si - ya - hamb' e - ku - kha - nyen' kwen - khos', si - ya -

march-ing in the light of God. We are march - ing in the
hamb' e - ku - kha - nyen' kwen - khos'. Si - ya - hamb' e - ku - kha -

light of God, we are march-ing in the light of God.
nyen' kwen - khos', si - ya - hamb' e - ku - kha-nyen' kwen - khos'.

We are march - ing, Oo we are
Si - ya - ham - ba, Oo si - ya -

march - ing in the light of God. We are march-ing,
hamb' e - ku - kha - nyen' kwen - khos'. Si - ya - ham - ba,

Oo we are march-ing in the light of God.
Oo si - ya - hamb' e - ku - kha-nyen' kwen - khos'.

38

With One Voice

Ricky Manalo

Verses

1. Take the Word and go out to ev - 'ry land:
2. Take the Word to our neigh - bor - hoods and streets:
3. Take the Word to the peo - ple in de - spair:
4. Take the Word to the na - tions ev - 'ry - where:

1-4. shine the light of Christ for all to see!

1. May the lives of those we touch sing
2. May we all set out to live in
3. May our ac - tions and our deeds bring
4. May the wit - ness of our lives trans -

1. praise to God a - bove. Let us sing, we'll sing:
2. peace and har - mo - ny. They will see and sing:
3. com - fort to their needs. And they'll know and sing:
4. form the world a - new. And we'll shine, we'll shine:

Refrain

With one voice we'll pass the Word a-long; with one

voice, bring jus-tice to the world. And with all the an -

- gels we'll spread the good-ness of God. With all pow-er and glo-

1-3

3 to Verses 2-4

- ry the Word of God shall reign.

4

to Refrain | Final

- ry the Word of God— - ry, with all pow -

- er and glo - ry, with all pow - er and glo -

- ry the Word of God shall reign!

39 You Are the Way

Steve Angrisano and Pat Smith

Refrain

You are the Way, you are the Truth, you are the Life, my sal-va-

-tion. You are the Way, you are the Truth, you are the

1-3 Life, the gate-way to my soul.

to Verses 4-5 -way to my soul. **to Refrain**

Final -way to my soul. You are the Life, the gate-way to my soul.

Verses 1, 2
1. We __ come to-geth-er now, we cel-e-brate and shout,
2. In a world that's mov-ing fast, we seek what will not last.

1. for you have shown the way.
2. We miss the nar-row road. But

1. We lift our voic-es high, we sing, we dance, we cry:
2. when we look in-side our-selves, we find that no one else

1. "You are the on-ly way!"
2. but you can make us whole. **to Refrain**

Verse 3
3. If we ask you we will re-ceive. If we seek you

3. then we shall find. Knock, and gates will be o-pened wide,

3. for a might-y God has done great things for you! **to Refrain**

Text © 1999, Steve Angrisano, Thomas N. Tomaszek and Christi Smith. Music © 1999, Steve Angrisano and Patrick Smith. Published by spiritandsong.com®, a division of OCP. All rights reserved.

Your Words, Lord, Are Spirit and Life
Psalm 19

Bob Hurd

Refrain

Your words, Lord, are Spir-it, Spir - it and life. life.

Verse 1

1. The law of the LORD is per-fect, re-fresh-ing the soul. The de-

1. cree of the LORD is trust-wor-thy, giv-ing wis-dom to the sim-ple.

Verses 2, 3

2. The pre-cepts of the LORD are right, re - joic-ing the heart;
3. The fear of the LORD is pure, en - dur-ing for - ev - er;

2. the com-mand of the LORD is clear, en-light-'ning the eye.
3. the stat-utes of the LORD are true, all of them just.

Verses 4, 5

4. They are more pre - cious than gold, than a
5. Let the words of my mouth and the

4. heap of pur - est gold; sweet - er al - so than
5. thought of my heart find fa - vor be-fore you, O

4. syr - up or hon - ey from the comb.
5. LORD, my rock and my re - deem - er.

41

My God, My God
Psalm 22

Timothy R. Smith

Refrain

My God, my God, why have you a - ban - doned me?

1 | 2-5 | to Verses | Final

Verse 1

1. All who see me scoff; they mock me with part - ed

1. lips, they wag their heads: "He re - lied on the LORD; let him de -

to Refrain

1. liv - er him, let him res - cue him, if he loves him."

Verse 2

2. In - deed man - y dogs sur - round me, a

2. pack of e - vil - do - ers close up - on me; they have

to Refrain

2. pierced my hands and feet, I can num - ber all my bones.

Verse 3

3. They di - vide my gar - ments a - mong them, for my

3. ves - ture they cast lots. But you, O LORD, be not

to Refrain

3. far from me; O my help, has - ten to my aid.

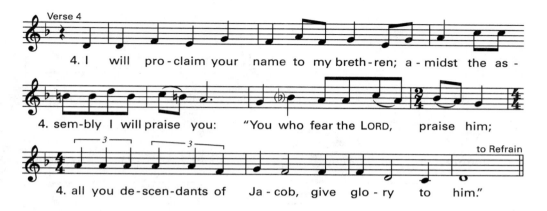

Verse 4

4. I will pro-claim your name to my breth-ren; a-midst the as-

4. sem-bly I will praise you: "You who fear the LORD, praise him;

to Refrain

4. all you de-scen-dants of Ja-cob, give glo-ry to him."

The Lord Is My Shepherd
Psalm 23

Joshua Blakesley

Refrain

The Lord is my shep - herd; there is

noth-ing I shall want. The Lord is my shep-

- herd; there is noth-ing I shall want.

| 1, 4 to Refrain | 2, 3 to Verses | Final | 3 |

I shall not want.

Verse 1

1. He lets me rest in o - pen fields so

1. green. He leads me to the qui - et streams.

1. He gives me strength and

1. guides me in his ways. He re-news his prom-

to Refrain

1. - is - es each day.

Verse 2

2. He is   my guide,   my shep-herd and   my

2. king,   and in   my fear   he of - fers   peace.

2. Though I   walk   through   the val - ley,   I

2. will   not be   a-fraid.   You will   pro - tect

to Refrain

2. me;   I'll   be   saved.

43

To You, O Lord
Psalm 25*

Timothy R. Smith

Refrain

To you, O Lord, I lift my soul, O Lord, I lift my

soul. soul. soul.

Verse 1

1. Your ways, O LORD, make known to me;

1. teach me your paths, guide me in your truth and

1. teach me, for you are God my sav-ior.

Verse 2

2. Good and up-right is the LORD; thus he

2. shows sin-ners the way. He guides the hum - ble to

2. jus - tice, and teach-es the hum-ble his way.

*For Psalm 27, see song #46.

3. All the paths of the LORD are kind-ness and con-stan-cy toward

3. those who keep his cov-e-nant and his de-crees. The

3

3. friend-ship of the LORD is with those who fear him,

to Refrain

3. and his cov-e-nant, for their in - struc-tion.

44

Taste and See

Psalm 34*

Steve Angrisano

Refrain

Taste and see the good-ness of the Lord, the good-ness of the Lord. Taste and see the good-ness of the Lord, the good-ness of the Lord. Lord. Lord. the good-ness of the Lord.

1-4 — 1: to Refrain / 2-4: to Verses — **Final**

Verse 1

1. I will bless the Lord at all times.
1. Praise will be on my lips. My soul will glo-
1. -ry in the Lord. The poor will hear and be glad.

Verse 2

2. I sought the Lord who an-swered me, de-
2. liv-ered me from my fear. Look to God that you might
2. shine with the ra - diance of God's joy.

*For Psalm 27, see song #46.

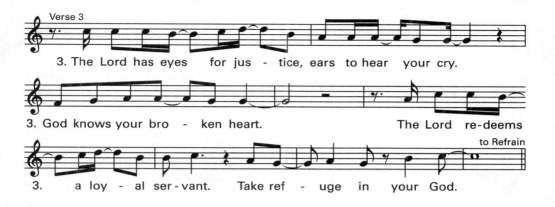

Verse 3

3. The Lord has eyes for jus - tice, ears to hear your cry.

3. God knows your bro - ken heart. The Lord re-deems

to Refrain

3. a loy - al ser - vant. Take ref - uge in your God.

Text: Based on Psalm 34:2–3, 5–6, 16, 19, 23. Refrain text © 1969, 1981, 1997, ICEL. All rights reserved. Used with permission.
Music and verses text © 2004, Steve Angrisano. Published by OCP. All rights reserved.

45 God Mounts His Throne
Psalm 47

Curtis Stephan

Refrain

(Ascension Psalm text) God mounts his throne to shouts of joy: a

(Common Psalm text) *God mounts his throne to shouts of joy, to*

blare of trum-pets for the Lord.   3. For

shouts, to shouts_____ of joy.

Verse 1

1. All you peo - ples, clap your hands, shout to God,

1. shout to God with cries of glad - ness.

1. For the Lord, the Most High, the awe - some,

3 to Refrain

1. is the great king o - ver all the earth.

Verse 2

2. God mounts his throne a - mid shouts of joy; the

2. Lord, a - mid trum-pet blasts. Sing praise to God,

2. to God, sing praise; sing

3 to Refrain

2. praise to our king, sing praise.

Verse 3

3. king of all the earth is God;

3. sing hymns of praise. God reigns o -

3. - ver all the na - tions,

3 to Refrain

3. God sits up-on his ho - ly throne.

The Lord Is My Light and My Salvation

Psalm 27

Jesse Manibusan

Refrain

The Lord is my light and my sal - va - tion; whom shall I fear? The Lord is my life, my life's ref - uge; of whom should I be a - fraid?

Verse 1

1. Hear, O Lord, the sound of my call; be gra - cious and an - swer me. For you, O Lord, my heart is long - ing. With all my heart your face I seek. *to Refrain*

Verse 2

2. Your pres - ence, O Lord, I seek; do not hide your face from me. Do not in an - ger turn a - way your ser - vant. You are my help; do not for - sake me. *to Refrain*

Verse 3

3. I be - lieve I shall see the good - ness of the Lord in the land of the liv - ing. Be strong; let your heart take cour - age. Wait for the Lord. *to Refrain*

Be Merciful, O Lord

Psalm 51

Steve Angrisano

Refrain

Be mer-ci-ful, O Lord. Have mer-cy on us, for we have sinned. We come be-fore you; cleanse us from with-in. Have mer-cy on us, Lord.

1 to Refrain *2-4* to Verses *Final*

Have mer-cy on us, Lord.

Verses

1. Have mer - cy on me in your good-ness, Lord.
2. Cre - ate a clean heart___ for me, O God.
3. Give me the joy of your sal - va - tion, Lord,

1. In your great com-pas-sion wipe out my of-fense.
2. And a stead - fast spir - it, re - new with-in me.
3. and a will - ing spir - it sus - tain with-in me.

1. Wash me from guilt, Lord,___ cleanse me from my sin.
2. Cast me not out from your pres - ence, O___ Lord.
3. O - pen my lips, let my mouth pro-claim your praise.

to Refrain

1. Have mer - cy on___ me, Lord.
2. Take not your Spir - it from me.
3. Have mer - cy on___ me, Lord.

48
My Soul Is Thirsting for You
Psalm 63

Andy Andino

Refrain

My soul is thirst-ing for you, O Lord my God; my soul is thirst-ing for you. My

soul is thirst-ing for you, O Lord my God; my

soul is thirst-ing.

1, Final to Refrain (Fine) | 2-5 to Verses

1. O

Verse 1

1. God, you are my God whom I seek; for

1. you my flesh pines and my soul thirsts

1. like the earth, parched, life-less and

to Refrain

1. with-out wa-ter.

Verse 2

2. Thus have I gazed toward you in the sanc-tu-ar-y

2. to see your pow-er and your glo-ry,

2. for your kind-ness is a great - er good than life;

to Refrain

2. my lips shall glo-ri-fy you.

Verse 3

3. Thus will I bless you while I live; lift-ing

3. up my hands, I will call up-on your name. As with the

3. rich-es of a ban - quet shall my soul be sat - is-fied,

to Refrain

3. and with ex - ul-tant lips my mouth shall praise you.

Verse 4

4. You are my help, and in the

4. shad-ow of your wings I shout for joy. My

4. soul clings fast to you; your

to Refrain

4. right hand up - holds me.

49

Let All the Earth Cry Out
Psalm 66

Bob Halligan Jr.

Refrain

Let all the earth cry out to God with joy, al-le-lu - ia.

Verses

1. Shout joy-ful - ly to God, all the earth, sing ___
2. "Let all on earth sing praise and wor - ship you, sing ___
3. ₹ He has changed the sea in - to dry land; through the
4. ₹ Hear ___ now, all you who fear God, while ___

1. praise ___ to the glo-ry of his name; pro-claim his glo-rious
2. praise ___ to the ho - li - est of names!" ₹ Come and see the
3. riv - er they passed ___ on foot. Let us re-joice in
4. I de-clare what he has done for me. ₹ Bless - ed be

to Refrain

1. praise. Say to God, __ "How tre - men-dous are your deeds!"
2. Lord's won-drous deeds a-mong the chil - dren of A - dam.
3. him. He ___ rules ___ by his might ___ for - ev - er.
4. God who re - fused me not my prayer ___ or his kind - ness.

50

Lord, Every Nation
Psalm 72

Jesse Manibusan

Refrain

Lord, ev-'ry na - tion on earth will a-dore you, O God.

Lord, ev-'ry na - tion on earth will a-dore you.

Verses 1, 4

1. En-dow our lead-ers, O God, with your judg - ment.
4. For you shall res - cue the poor when they cry out,

1. And with your jus - tice on ev - 'ry - one.
4. and the af - flict - ed when help can't be found.

1. For you gov - ern your peo - ple with jus - tice, ___
4. You shall raise up the low - ly ___ and the poor,

to Refrain

1. and your af - flict - ed ones with right-eous - ness.
4. and those on high ___ shall be cast ___ down.

Verse 2

2. Jus-tice shall flow - er in your days, and peace till the moon

2. be no more. May your king-dom reach from sea to sea,

to Refrain

2. and from the riv - er to the ends of the earth.

Verse 3

3. Tar - shish and the Isles shall bring trib-ute, gifts from

3. Se - ba and A - ra - bi - a. All oth-er pow-ers shall pay

to Refrain

3. their hom - age, and ev-'ry na-tion shall serve the Lord.

51 Lord, Show Us Your Mercy and Love
Psalm 85

Janet Sullivan Whitaker

Refrain

Lord, show us your mer-cy and love.

Show us your mer-cy, show us your love. *to Verses*

Last time Show us your mer-cy, show us your love. *Repeat as needed*

Verse 1 *Cantor*

1. I will hear what you pro-claim: words of peace for all.

All

1. Show us your mer-cy, show us your love.

Cantor

1. You are al-ways near to those who seek sal-va-tion.

All

1. Show us your mer-cy, show us your love. *to Refrain*

Verse 2 *Cantor*

2. How your glo-ry fills the earth, flow-ing through our land!

All

2. Show us your mer-cy, show us your love.

Cantor

2. Kind-ness and truth shall meet, peace and jus-tice kiss.

2. Show us your mer - cy, show us your love.

Verse 3

Cantor

3. Foun-tains of truth shall spring up fresh from the earth.

All

3. Show us your mer - cy, show us your love.

Cantor

3. Jus-tice shall smile up-on the earth from up in heav - en.

All to Refrain

3. Show us your mer - cy, show us your love.

Verse 4

4. You pro-vide ev - 'ry-thing we need. Oh,

4. you pro-vide a land that gives us food.

4. Ho - ly God, let jus - tice walk be-fore you, and

to Refrain

4. peace will light the way.

52 Be with Me, Lord

Psalm 91

Sarah Hart and Curtis Stephan

Refrain

Be with me, Lord, when I am in trou - ble. Be with me, Lord, be with me.

1, Final / *2-5 to Verses* / **Verse 1**

1. You who rest in the shad - ow of the Lord and a - bide in the pres - ence of God, 1. say with your heart, "My shel - ter and strength, 1. my God, in you I trust."

to Refrain

Verse 2

2. E - vil will not fall up - on you; no af - flic - tion will find 2. your door. For the an - gels have been sent to pro - tect 2. you, and guard you in all your ways.

to Refrain

3. If you stum - ble they will catch you; they will keep you from fall-

3. - ing down. From the den of the li - on and the

3. threat of the snake you will es - cape un-harmed.

Verse 4

4. Call and I will an - swer, says the Lord, trust and know

4. I am here. Cling to me with your life:

4. there is noth-ing you should fear.

53

If Today
Psalm 95

Trevor Thomson

Refrain
If to-day you hear God's voice, hard-en not your hearts.

to Verses | Last time
Hard-en not your hearts.

Verse 1
1. Come, let us sing joy-ful-ly to the Lord;
1. Let us ac-claim the Rock of our sal-
1. va - tion. Let us greet God with thanks-
1. giv - ing; Let us joy - ful - ly sing,
to Refrain
1. let us joy - ful-ly sing psalms to him.

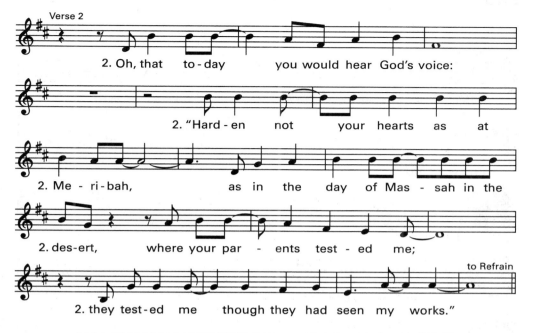

Verse 2

2. Oh, that to-day you would hear God's voice:

2. "Hard-en not your hearts as at

2. Me - ri - bah, as in the day of Mas - sah in the

2. des-ert, where your par - ents test - ed me;

to Refrain

2. they test-ed me though they had seen my works."

All the Ends of the Earth
Psalm 98

Ken Canedo

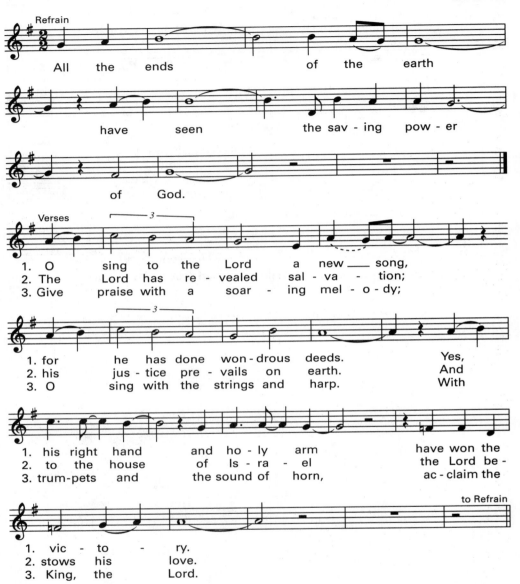

Refrain

All the ends of the earth

have seen the sav - ing pow - er

of God.

Verses

1. O sing to the Lord a new ___ song,
2. The Lord has re - vealed sal - va - tion;
3. Give praise with a soar - ing mel - o - dy;

1. for he has done won - drous deeds. Yes,
2. his jus - tice pre - vails on earth. And
3. O sing with the strings and harp. With

1. his right hand and ho - ly arm have won the
2. to the house of Is - ra - el the Lord be -
3. trum - pets and the sound of horn, ac - claim the

to Refrain

1. vic - to - ry.
2. stows his love.
3. King, the Lord.

We Are His People

Psalm 100

Greg Walton

Refrain

We are his peo - ple, we are his peo - ple,

we are his peo - ple: the sheep of his flock.

Verse 1

1. Sing joy-ful - ly un-to the LORD, all you lands; serve the LORD with

to Refrain

1. glad - ness; come be-fore him with joy-ful song.

Verse 2

2. Know that the LORD is God; he made us, his we

to Refrain

2. are; his peo-ple, the flock he tends.

Verse 3

3. Know that the LORD is good: his kind-ness en-dures for-

to Refrain

3. ev-er, and his faith-ful-ness, to all gen - er - a-tions.

56

The Lord Is Kind and Merciful

Psalm 103

Rick Modlin

Refrain

The Lord is kind, the Lord is kind and mer - ci-ful. The Lord is kind and mer - ci - ful, mer - ci - ful; mer - ci - ful is the Lord.

1, 6 *2-5, Final* *to Verses*

Verses

1. O __ my soul, bless the Lord and praise his ho -
2. God __ for-gives, heal - ing all our pain and sin -
3. Full __ of grace, full of mer - cy and a - bun -
4. Far as the east from the west, God placed our sin

1. - ly name. Bless the Lord, _____ O my soul;
2. - ful - ness; saves us from __ an emp - ty life,
3. - dant love, slow to an - ger is the Lord;
4. from us. God's com - pas - sion rests on us

to Refrain

1. keep in mind what God has done for me.
2. cov - ers us with gen - tle - ness and love.
3. God does not re - pay us for our sins.
4. like a fa - ther's mer - cy for his own.

Lord, Send Out Your Spirit

Psalm 104

Craig Colson

Refrain

O Lord, send out your Spir - it, and re-new the face of the earth,

re-new the face of the earth.

1, 3, 5 | **2, 4, Final** to Verses

Verse 1

1. Bless the LORD, O my soul! O LORD, my God, how great you are

1. in-deed! You are clothed with maj-es - ty and glo - ry. *to Refrain*

Verse 2

2. Man-y are your works, O LORD! In your just - ice you

2. have made them known. You trav-el on the wings of the wind, *to Refrain*

2. O bless the LORD, my soul!

This Is the Day
Psalm 118

Bobby Fisher

Refrain

This is the day! This is the day!

This is the day that the Lord has made!

Let us re-joice! Let us re-joice!

Let us re-joice and be

1. glad! *2-5* glad! *to Verses* *Final* glad!

Let us re-joice and be glad!

Verse 1

1. This is the day that the Lord has made. *to Refrain*

1. Let us re-joice and be glad.

Verse 2

2. Give thanks to the Lord! Our God is good,

2. whose love en-dures for-ev - er.

2. Let all the chil - dren of Is - rael say:

to Refrain

2. God's love en - dures for - ev - er.

Verse 3

3. The right hand of God has struck with pow'r. The

3. right hand of God is ex - alt - ed.

3. I shall not die, but I shall live

to Refrain

3. and pro - claim the works of the Lord!

Verse 4

4. The stone which the build - ers re - ject - ed has be -

4. come the foun - da - tion of our house!

4. By the Lord has this been done. How

to Refrain

4. won - der-ful to be - hold!

Text: Psalm 118:24, 1–2, 16–17, 22–23. Refrain text © 1969, 1981, ICEL. All rights reserved. Used with permission.
Verses text © 1970, 1997, 1998, CCD. All rights reserved. Used with permission. Music © 1994, Bobby Fisher. Published by OCP. All rights reserved.

59

I Rejoiced
Psalm 122

Trevor Thomson

Refrain

I re - joiced when I heard them say:

let us go to the house of the Lord.

I re - joiced when I heard them say:

let us go to the house of the Lord.

Verses

1. I re - joiced when they said to me: ____
2. Strong - ly built is Je - ru - sa - lem, ____
3. For the love of ____ friends and fam - 'ly,

1. "Let us go to the house of the Lord to - day."
2. strong - ly built with ___ u - ni - ty and love.
3. may the peace of God be ___ with you ___ al - ways.

1. And now we stand _____ with - in your gates;
2. And it is there _____ that the tribes go up,
3. For the love _____ of God's house,

to Refrain

1. my ___ heart is glad and I ___ will sing with joy.
2. go ___ up ___ to the moun - tain of our God.
3. I will pray for you, will pray ____ for your good.

With the Lord There Is Mercy

Psalm 130

Rick Modlin

Refrain

With the Lord there is mer - cy, and full - ness of re - demp - tion.

With the Lord there is mer - cy, and full - ness of re - demp - tion.

Verse 1

1. Out of the depths I cry to you, O Lord; Lord, hear my voice!

1. Let your ears be at - ten - tive to my voice in sup - pli - ca - tion.

Verse 2

2. If you, Lord, mark our in - iq - ui - ties, Lord, who can stand?

2. But with you is for - give - ness, and so you may be re - vered.

Verse 3

3. I trust in the Lord; my soul trusts in his word. My soul

3. waits for the Lord more than sen - t'nels wait for the dawn.

Verse 4

4. For with the Lord is kind - ness and with him is plen - teous re -

4. demp - tion; and he will re - deem Is - ra - el from all their in - iq - ui - ties.

Psalms

61 God's Love Is Everlasting

Psalm 136

Tom Tomaszek

Refrain

God's love is ev-er-last-ing, faith-ful till the end of time. God's
love is ev-er-last-ing, God's love will nev-er end. *(1-3 to Verses)* *(Final)* end.

Verses

1. Give___ thanks to the Lord,___ for___ God___ is good. Give
2. Who cre-at-ed the earth,___ who di-vid-ed the seas, who
3. Who a-lone does great won-ders, who___ frees us from harm, who

1. thanks to the Lord___ of Lords. Give
2. set___ the heav-en-ly lights. The
3. nour-ish-es all liv-ing things. Give

1. thanks to the___ God a-bove oth-er gods.
2. sun to rule the day, the stars___ at night. } God's
3. thanks to the___ God of heav-en and earth.

(to Refrain)

1-3. mer-cy en-dures for-ev - er.

The Lord Is Near/I Will Praise Your Name

Psalm 145*

62

Tom Booth

Refrain

The Lord is near to all who call___ him.

Common Psalm text: I will praise your name for - ev - er,

The Lord is near to all who call in truth. truth.

I will praise my king___ and my God. God.

Verse 1

1. Ev-'ry day will I bless you, I will praise your name for - ev - er and

1. ev - er. Great is the Lord and high-ly to be praised.

Verse 2

2. His great-ness is un-search-a - ble. The Lord is gra-cious and

2. mer-ci-ful, slow to an - ger and of great kind - ness.

Verse 3

3. The Lord is good to all and com-pas-sion-ate toward all his works.

3. The Lord is just in all his ways and ho - ly in all his works.

*For Psalm 141, see song #63.

63 Lord, Let My Prayer Arise/Suba Mi Oración

Psalm 141

Bob Hurd

Refrain

LORD, let my prayer a-rise, rise up like in-cense in-to your pres-ence, in-to your pres-ence. *Su-ba mi o-ra-ción co-mo in-cien-so en tu pre-sen-cia, en tu pre-sen-cia.*

English Verses

1. From the depths of my heart I thank ___ you, O
2. I will bow my-self down be - fore your ho - ly
3. I called out and you heard, you an - swered my
4. For the LORD dwells on high, yet cares ___ for the
5. In the face of my foes you safe - guard my

1. LORD; ___ be - fore all the an - gels I
2. tem - ple, praie - ing your name for your
3. cry; ___ you filled me with cour - age and
4. poor, ___ lift - ing the low - ly and
5. life; ___ out - stretched is your hand to pro -

to Refrain

1. sing ___ out your praise.
2. con - stan - cy and love.
3. strength - ened my soul.
4. hum - bling the proud.
5. tect ___ me, O LORD.

Note: The entire Refrain may be sung in English by switching the language of the 2nd half of the Refrain to English.

Spanish Verses

1. Te doy gra - cias, Se - ñor, _____ de
2. Yo ven - dré _____ a pos - trar - me an - te tu
3. Me es - cu - chas - te, Se - ñor, _____ cuan - do
4. El Se - ñor _____ es su - bli - me, _____ se
5. Si me en - cuen - tro en - tre pe - li - gros, me con -

1. to - do co - ra - zón; _____ ⸲ de - lan - te de los
2. san - to _____ tem - plo, _____ ⸲ dán - do - te
3. yo _____ te in - vo - qué _____ ⸲ y dis - te a mi
4. fi - ja en el hu - mil - de; ⸲ A a - quel _____ que es so -
5. ser - vas la vi - da. ⸲ Tu bra - zo me

to Refrain

1. án - ge - les ta - ñe - ré _____ pa - ra ti. _____
2. gra - cias _ por tu a - mor y le - al - tad. _____
3. al - ma _ más _ va - lor. _____
4. ber - bio lo mi - ra des - de le - jos. _____
5. sal - va _ de mis e - ne - mi - gos. _

Text: Refrain based on Psalm 141:2; verses based on Psalm 138:1–2ab, 3, 6, 7; Spanish verses tr. by Jaime Cortez.
Text and music © 2001, Bob Hurd. Published by OCP. All rights reserved.

64 Bread for the World

Bernadette Farrell

Refrain: All

Bread for the world: a world of hun-ger. Wine for all peo-ples: peo-ple who thirst. May we who eat be bread for oth-ers. May we who drink pour out our love.

Verses: Cantor

1. Lord Je-sus Christ, you are the bread of life, bro-ken to
2. Lord Je-sus Christ, you are the wine of peace, poured in-to
3. Lord Je-sus Christ, you call us to your feast, at which the

1. reach and heal the wounds of hu-man pain. Where we di-
2. hearts once bro-ken and where dry-ness sleeps. Where we are
3. rich and pow'r-ful have be-come the least. Where we sur-

1. vide your peo-ple, you are wait-ing there
2. tired and wea-ry, you are wait-ing there
3. vive on oth-ers in our hu-man greed,

to Refrain

1. on bend-ed knee to wash our feet with end-less care.
2. to be the way which beck-ons us be-yond de-spair.
3. you walk a-mong us beg-ging for your ev-'ry need.

Bread of Life/Pan de Vida

Jaime Cortez

65

Refrain

Bread of Life, Pan de Vi-da,

Wine of Love, Vi-no de A-mor.

All as one bod-y, to-dos u-ni-dos,

at the ta-ble of God, en la me-sa de Dios.

Verses

1. Fed from the grape and grain, we nur-ture our faith in you.
2. *To-dos en el al-tar for-ma-mos un so-lo ser.*
3. So man-y hopes and fears are placed in your hands, O God.
4. *Guí-a nues-tro ca-mi-no, da-nos tu pro-tec-ción*

1. We are your chil-dren, proof of your prom-ise,
2. *So-mos el Cuer-po de Je-su-cris-to,*
3. Blend-ing our sto-ries with your com-pas-sion
4. *mien-tras tra-e-mos tu san-to rei-no*

to Refrain

1. fruit of your love. _____
2. *u-no con Dios.* _____
3. brings us new life. _____
4. *a to-do el mun-do.* _____

Communion

66 Come to the Lord

Steve Angrisano and Tom Tomaszek

Verses

1. Do not let your hearts be trou - bled.
2. I will nev - er leave you or - phans;
3. Eat this bread and nev - er hun - ger;

1. Chil - dren, do not fear. Though you suf - fer as
2. you are not a - lone. I have made your place
3. I will give you life. Drink the cup I place

1. I suf - fered, I am al - ways near.
2. in heav - en, in my fa - ther's home.
3. be - fore you; you will nev - er die.

Refrain

Come to the Lord; come to the ta - ble of last -

- ing life. Bring your bur - dens; there's no price, just

to Verses | Last time

come to the Lord. Come to the Lord.

Communion

Come to the Water

John Foley, S.J.
Arranged by Matt Maher

1. O let all who thirst, let them come to the wa-ter.
2. And let all who seek, let them come to the wa-ter.
3. And let all who toil, let them come to the wa-ter.
4. And let all the poor, let them come to the wa-ter.

1. And let all who have noth-ing, let them come to the
2. And let all who have noth-ing, let them come to the
3. And let all who are wea-ry, let them come to the
4. Bring the ones who are lad-en, bring them all to the

1. Lord: with-out mon-ey, with-out price.
2. Lord: with-out mon-ey, with-out strife.
3. Lord: all who la-bor, with-out rest.
4. Lord: bring the chil-dren with-out might.

1-3

1. Why should you pay the price, ex-cept for the Lord?
2. Why should you spend your life, ex-cept for the Lord?
3. How can your soul find rest, ex-cept for the Lord?
4. Eas-y the load and

2   Final   3

1-3.   4. light: come to the Lord.

3

4.   Come to the Lord.   I will run to you.

4. I will run to you. I will run to you, my Lord.

Communion

68 Here at This Table

Janet Sullivan Whitaker and Max Whitaker

Refrain

Come and be filled here at this ta-ble.

Food for all who hun-ger and drink for all who thirst.

Drink of his love, wine of sal - va - tion.

You shall live for - ev - er in Je - sus Christ the

1-5 to Verses / **Final**

Lord. Lord. You shall live for -

ev - er in Je - sus Christ the Lord.

Verses 1, 2, 4

1. You who la - bor for jus - tice, you who la - bor for
2. You with lives full of pain, you who sor - row and
4. You, the a - ged a - mong us, ho - ly, faith-ful and

1. peace, you who stead - y the plow in the
2. weep, you, be - lov - ed of Christ, come to
4. wise, may the wis - dom you share form our

to Refrain

1. field of the Lord!
2. him, come to him!
4. lives and our world!

Communion

Verses 3, 5

3. Chil - dren of ev - 'ry col - or ___ in ev - 'ry land,
5. Let each wom - an and man ___ learn from the strang-er;

3. you are his own, he gath-ers you gent - ly.
5. we're not so dif - f'rent and so much u - nites us.

3. Don't you grow wea - ry, ___ for when you
5. For we are one, ___ blest with the

to Refrain

3. run, 𝄾 you run with the Lord!
5. Spir - it and the pow - er of love!

Communion

69   Feed Us, Lord

Larry Theiss and Carey Landry

Round
Refrain

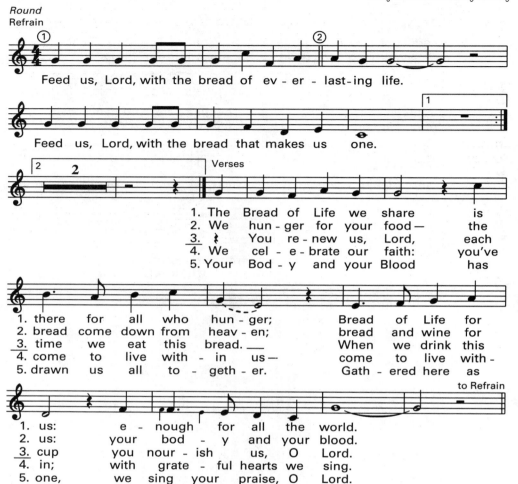

① Feed us, Lord, with the bread of ev - er - last-ing life.

② Feed us, Lord, with the bread that makes us one.

Verses

1. The Bread of Life we share is
2. We hun - ger for your food— the
3. 𝄾 You re - new us, Lord, each
4. We cel - e - brate our faith: you've
5. Your Bod - y and your Blood has

1. there for all who hun - ger;   Bread of Life for
2. bread come down from heav - en;   bread and wine for
3. time we eat this bread. ___   When we drink this
4. come to live with - in us—   come to live with -
5. drawn us all to - geth - er.   Gath - ered here as

to Refrain

1. us: e - nough for all the world.
2. us: your bod - y and your blood.
3. cup   you nour - ish us, O Lord.
4. in;   with grate - ful hearts we sing.
5. one,   we sing your praise, O Lord.

I Sought the Lord

70

Tom Booth

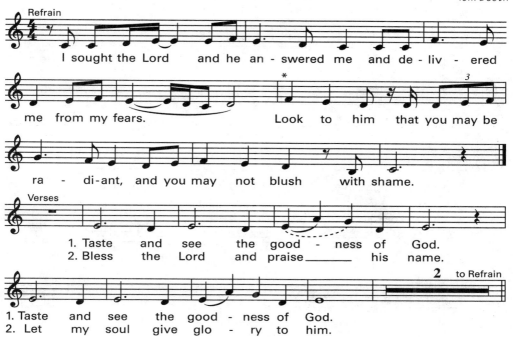

Refrain

I sought the Lord and he an-swered me and de-liv-ered me from my fears. Look to him that you may be ra-di-ant, and you may not blush with shame.

Verses

1. Taste and see the good-ness of God.
2. Bless the Lord and praise_____ his name.

2 to Refrain

1. Taste and see the good-ness of God.
2. Let my soul give glo-ry to him.

*Last time: Repeat final phrase.

71   Like the Bread

Tom Booth

Refrain

Like the bread, we are tak-en. Like the Christ, we are blessed. On this al-tar we are bro-ken, giv'n as food that all might live, giv'n as food that all might live.

Verse 1

1. How quick-ly we re-ject our-selves, blind-ed from our call. We re-
1. sign to live in fear of love, of self, of all. This is
1. not the will of God for the cho-sen must be free. We are
1. tak-en by the love of Christ to live e-ter-nal-ly.

Verse 2

2. Bro-ken like the bread of life, we of-ten flee from pain. We re-
2. sign to live our lives, not know-ing death's true gain. This is
2. not the will of God, for in dy-ing we will live. The
2. cross, a sign of vic-to-ry and of the heal-ing it will give.

Communion

Some say it is good to have, but the faith-ful learn to give. Like the saints of old who lived pre-pared, we be-come like Christ— to feed, to share.

to Refrain

One Bread, One Body

72

John Foley, S.J.

Refrain

One bread, one bod-y, one Lord of all, one cup of bless-ing which we bless. And we, though man-y, through-out the earth, we are one bod-y in this one Lord.

Verses

1. Gen-tile or Jew, ser-vant or
2. Man-y the gifts, man-y the
3. Grain for the fields, scat-tered and

to Refrain

1. free, wom-an or man, no more.
2. works, one in the Lord of all!
3. grown, gath-ered to one, for all.

Communion

73

One Bread, One Cup

Bobby Fisher, Greg Lee,
Craig Aven and Ken Canedo

Verse 1

1. We all come be-fore you now, hun-gry for

1. your heal-ing touch. Here we stand with o-pen

1. hearts, thirst-ing for your love.

1. You are the one who fills our ev-'ry need. So

1. with one voice we lift our hearts in u-ni-ty.

Refrain

One bread, one cup, one bod-y of Christ, u-nit-ed in love.

One bread, one cup, one liv-ing sac-ri-fice poured out in your blood.

Ho-ly Spir-it, re-new us, that in each oth-er we may see you.

1, 2 — 3 —
1: to Verse 2
2: to Bridge

Gath-ered as one fam-'ly in love, one bread, one cup.

Final — 3 —

Gath-ered as one fam-'ly in love, one bread, one cup.

Communion

Verse 2

2. As we gath - er at your ta - ble,

2. bro-ken like the bread we share, fill our hearts

2. with your com-pas-sion for a world in need of care.

2. You are the way. You are the life. You are the truth. The

to Refrain

2. source of our sal-va - tion, we find new life in you.

Bridge

When we go forth from this place of per - fect peace,

to Refrain

may your light shine in our lives for all the world to see.

Communion

74

Pan de Vida

Bob Hurd

Refrain

Bilingual: *Pan de Vi - da, cuer-po del Se - ñor,
Spanish: *Pan de Vi - da, cuer-po del Se - ñor,*

cup of bless - ing, blood of Christ the Lord.
san-ta co - pa, Cris-to Re - den-tor.

At this ta - ble the last shall be first.
Su jus - ti - cia nos con-ver-ti - rá.

**Po - der es ser-vir, por-que Dios es a - mor.
Po - der es ser-vir, por-que Dios es a - mor.

1-3 (to Verses) / **4** / **Final 3** / **Verses**

Po -
Po -

1. We are the
2. You call me
3. There is no
1. So-mos el
2. Us - te - des me
3. No hay es-

1. dwell-ing of God, _____ fra-gile and wound-ed and weak. __
2. Teach - er and Lord; _____ I, who have washed __ your feet. __
3. Jew ___ or Greek; _____ there is no slave ___ or free; __
1. tem - plo de Dios, _____ frá - gi - les se - res hu - ma -
2. lla - man "Se - ñor". _____ Me in - cli - no a la - var - les los pies. __
3. cla - vos ni li - bres, no hay mu - je - res ni hom -

1. _____ We are the bod - y of Christ, called to
2. _____ So you must do as I do, so the
3. _____ there is no wom - an or man; on - ly
1. *nos.* So - mos el cuer - po de Cris - to, lla -
2. _____ Ha - gan lo mis - mo, hu - mil - des, sir -
3. *bres,* só - lo a - que - llos que he - re - dan el

*Bread of Life, body of the Lord,
**Power is for service, because God is love.

Communion

1. be _____ the com-pas-sion of God. _____
2. great - est must be-come __ the least. _____
3. heirs _____ of the prom-ise of God. _____

1. *ma* - *dos a ser com-pa - si - vos.*
2. *vién* - *do - se u - nos a o - tros.*
3. *rei* - *no que Dios pro - me - tió.* _____

Table of Plenty

75

Dan Schutte

Refrain

Come to the feast of heav-en and earth! Come to the ta- ble of plen - ty! God will pro-vide for all that we need, here at the ta - ble of plen - ty.

Verses

1. O come and sit at my ta - ble where saints and
2. O come and eat with-out mon-ey; come to
3. My bread will ev - er sus-tain you through days of
4. Your fields will flow - er in full-ness; your homes will

1. sin - ners are friends. I wait to wel-come the lost and
2. drink with - out price. My feast of glad-ness will feed your
3. sor - row and woe. My wine will flow like a sea of
4. flour - ish in peace. For I, the giv - er of home and

to Refrain

1. lone - ly to share the cup of my love.
2. spir - it with faith and full - ness of life.
3. glad-ness to flood the depths of your soul.
4. har - vest, will send my rain on the soil.

76   Table of Life

Steve Angrisano

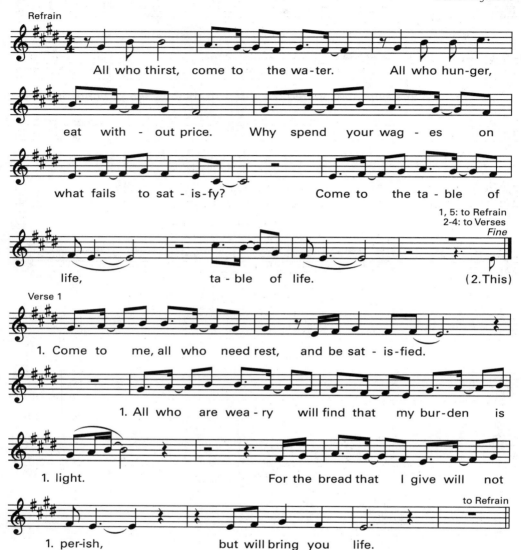

Refrain

All who thirst, come to the wa-ter. All who hun-ger,

eat with - out price. Why spend your wag - es on

what fails to sat-is-fy? Come to the ta - ble of

1, 5: to Refrain
2-4: to Verses
Fine

life, ta - ble of life. (2.This)

Verse 1

1. Come to me, all who need rest, and be sat - is-fied.

1. All who are wea - ry will find that my bur-den is

1. light. For the bread that I give will not

to Refrain

1. per-ish, but will bring you life.

Verse 2

2. bread that I break is my flesh, take and eat.

2. This cup now poured out is my blood for a world in need.

2. I lay down my life so you

to Refrain

2. might come and fol - low me.

Verse 3

3. Dance now with joy be - fore God whose mer - cy runs free.

3. The moun - tains will break in - to song for a might - y king.

3. The trees will clap hands for our

to Refrain

3. God. God is great in - deed!

77 The Eyes and Hands of Christ

Refrain

Where two or three are gath-ered in my name,

love will be found, life will a-bound.

By name we are called, from wa-ter we are sent:

1, 2 · to Verses 1, 2

to be-come the eyes and hands of Christ.

3 · to Verse 3 · Final

to be-come the eyes and hands of Christ.

Verses 1, 2

1. One we be-come, no long-er strang-ers. No long-er
2. One in the Spir-it, one in the Lord. One in the

1. emp-ty ___ or frail. Filled with the Spir-it, ev-'ry
2. break-ing of the bread. Life-giv-ing wit-ness of our

to Refrain

1. hun-ger sat-is-fied. Christ is the cen-ter of our lives.
2. dy-ing and new life, held by the prom-ise in our hands.

Communion

Verse 3

3. Not what we are, but what we be-come. Not what we

3. say, but what we do. Liv-ing the chal-lenge as

to Refrain

3. bear-ers of light. We are the eyes and hands of Christ.

Taste and See — 78
Bob Hurd

Refrain

Taste and see, O taste and see, taste and see the

good-ness of God.

Verses 1, 2

1. Glo-ry, glo-ry to God most high,
2. Who has fash-ioned the earth and sky,

1. glo-ry, bless-ing and praise. With one voice, O peo-ple, re-
2. who cre-a-ted the deep, who ex-alts the low-ly and

to Refrain

1. joice in our God, who hears the cry of all in need. O
2. sets cap-tives free, who o-pens the door to all those who seek. O

Verse 3

3. Oh, the love of God! Be-come flesh of our flesh,

to Refrain

3. so that we might live in glo - ry. O

Communion

We Are One Body

Dana

Refrain

We are one bod - y, one bod - y in Christ;

and we do not stand a - lone. We are one bod -

- y, one bod - y in Christ; and he

1-3, 5, 6 — **to Verses**

came that we might have life. Vss. 1-3 (For he tells us)

4, 7 — **to Refrain** — **Final**

He came that we might have life.

Verses 1, 2, 4, 5

1. When you eat my bod - y and you drink my blood, I will
2. Can you hear them cry - ing, can you feel their pain? Will you
4. I have come, your Sav - ior, that you might have life, through the
5. At the name of Je - sus ev - 'ry knee shall bend; Je - sus

1. live in you_____ and you will live in my love. When you
2. feed my hun - gry, will you help____ my lame? See the
4. tears____ and sor - row, through the toils____ and strife. Lis - ten
5. is____ the Lord____ and he will come____ a - gain. At the

1. eat my bod - y and you drink my blood, I will live in you_____
2. un-born ba - by, the for - got - ten one, they are not for-sak -
4. when I call you, for I know your need, come to me,__ your shep -
5. name of Je - sus ev - 'ry knee shall bend; Je - sus is____ the Lord__

1, 2 — **to Refrain** — **3, 4** — **to Refrain**

1. __ and you will live in my love.
2. - en, they are not__ un - loved.
4. - herd, for my   4. flock I feed.
5. __ and he will   5. come a - gain.

Communion

Verse 3: Solo/Choir

3. I am the Way, the Truth, the Life, I am the

3. Fi - nal Sac - ri - fice, I am the Way, the Truth, the

1
3. Life; he who be - lieves in me will have e - ter - nal life.

2
to Verse 4
3
3. Life; he who be - lieves in me will have e - ter - nal life.

Verse 6
Solo
6. On the rock of Pe -

All
We are one bod - y;

6. - ter, see my Church I build.

and we do not stand a -

6. Come re - ceive my spir - it, with my gifts be filled.

lone.

6. For you are my bod - y, you're my hands and

We are one bod - y;

6. feet.

and he came that we might have life.

6. Speak my word of life to ev - 'ry one you meet.

to Refrain

Communion

Bob Hurd

Communion

Come, Now Is the Time to Worship

Brian Doerksen

81

1. Come, now is the time to worship.
2. Come, just as you are to worship.

1. Come, now is the time to give your
2. Come, just as you are before your

1. heart. 2. God. Come.

One day ev-'ry tongue will con-fess you are God.

One day ev-'ry knee will bow.

Still the great-est trea-sure re-mains for those who glad-

to beginning

-ly choose you now.

82

Able

Sarah Hart

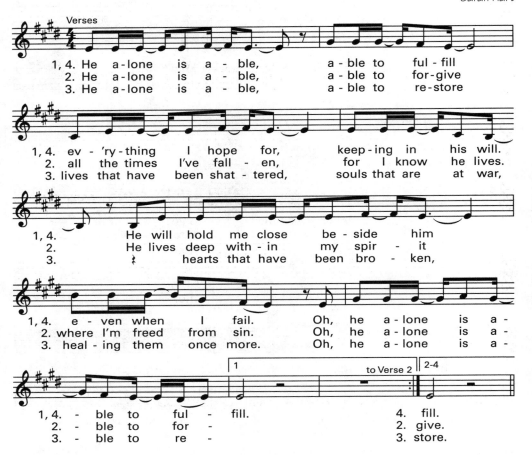

Verses

1, 4. He a-lone is a - ble, a - ble to ful - fill
2. He a-lone is a - ble, a - ble to for-give
3. He a-lone is a - ble, a - ble to re-store

1, 4. ev - 'ry-thing I hope for, keep-ing in his will.
2. all the times I've fall - en, for I know he lives.
3. lives that have been shat - tered, souls that are at war,

1, 4. He will hold me close be - side him
2. He lives deep with - in my spir - it
3. hearts that have been bro - ken,

1, 4. e - ven when I fail. Oh, he a - lone is a -
2. where I'm freed from sin. Oh, he a - lone is a -
3. heal - ing them once more. Oh, he a - lone is a -

1 | to Verse 2 | **2-4**

1, 4. - ble to ful - fill. 4. fill.
2. - ble to for - 2. give.
3. - ble to re - 3. store.

A - ble, my God is a - ble,

a - ble to set my spir - it free.

Look - ing past my fail - ures, down in - to

my heart, he is a - ble to love

1, 2 — to Verses 3, 4 — Final

me.   me.

He is a - ble to love me.

He is a - ble to love me.

Alabaré

Manuel José Alonso and José Pagán

Refrain

A - la - ba - ré, a - la - ba - ré, a -
O come and sing! O come and sing! Come,

la - ba - ré a mi Se - ñor. A - la - ba - ré, (a - la - ba -
sing your prais - es to the Lord. O come and sing! (O come and

ré,) a - la - ba - ré, (a - la - ba - ré,) a -
sing!) O come and sing! (O come and sing!) Come,

1-3 / **to Verses** / **Final**

la - ba - ré a mi Se - ñor. ñor.
sing your prais - es to the Lord. Lord.

Estrofas/Verses

1. Juan vio el nú - me - ro de los re - di - mi - dos
2. To - dos u - ni - dos, ___ a - le - gres can - ta - mos
3. So - mos tus hi - jos, ___ Dios ___ Pa - dre e - ter - no,

1. All of the faith - ful ___ were gath - ered 'round the ta - ble,
2. All were u - nit - ed ___ in joy - ful cel - e - bra - tion
3. Filled with the Spir - it, ___ they cried with ex - al - ta - tion:
4. We now in - her - it ___ the joy of the dis - ci - ples,

1. y to - dos a - la - ba - ban al Se - ñor.
2. glo - ria y a - la - ban - zas al Se - ñor.
3. Tú nos has cre - a - do por a - mor.

1. in mind and spir - it one in true ac - cord.
2. all through the night un - til the morn - ing sun,
3. "The love of God is here a - mong us all!
4. we sing and dance and of - fer con - stant praise.

Praise & Worship

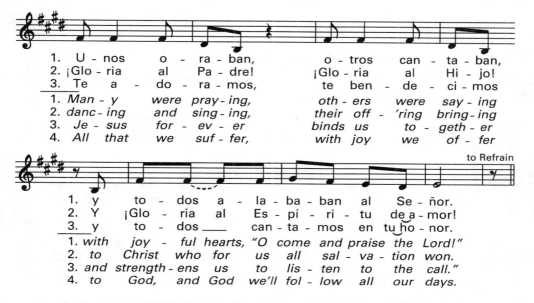

1. U - nos o - ra - ban, o - tros can - ta - ban,
2. ¡Glo - ria al Pa - dre! ¡Glo - ria al Hi - jo!
3. Te a - do - ra - mos, te ben - de - ci - mos

1. Man - y were pray - ing, oth - ers were say - ing
2. danc - ing and sing - ing, their off - 'ring bring - ing
3. Je - sus for - ev - er binds us to - geth - er
4. All that we suf - fer, with joy we of - fer

to Refrain

1. y to - dos a - la - ba - ban al Se - ñor.
2. Y ¡Glo - ria al Es - pí - ri - tu de a - mor!
3. y to - dos ___ can - ta - mos en tu ho - nor.

1. with joy - ful hearts, "O come and praise the Lord!"
2. to Christ who for us all sal - va - tion won.
3. and strength - ens us to lis - ten to the call."
4. to God, and God we'll fol - low all our days.

Text: Based on Revelation 7:4, 9–12. English tr. by Owen Alstott. Text and music © 1979, 2003, Manuel José Alonso and José Pagán.
Published by OCP. All rights reserved.

84   All Glory to God

Kathy Troccoli, Robert White Johnson
and William Cuomo

1. Ev-'ry-thing I say and do, ev-'ry-thing I am to you, oh, I

1. pray that you will know.

1. What-ev-er is good in me, where-ev-er there's

1. joy to see, hear me say, "It's not my own."

Refrain

All glo-ry to God, all hon-or is his, no oth-er is worth-

-y of his name. All glo-ry to God, I'll al-ways be his,

1, 3
for-ev-er I'll live to sing his praise.

1: to Verse 2   *2, 4*   *Final*
2: to Bridge   *to Refrain*

to sing his praise. to sing his praise.

to sing his praise.

to sing his praise.

Verse 2

2. Ev-'ry-day I know I'm blessed just to know my heart, it rests in his

2. hands that gave me life. But you know I

2. won't for-get what he's done for me, you bet I'm a-

2. mazed ev-'ry time. So I'm sing-ing...

Bridge 2

Ev-'ry-thing I say and do, ev-'ry-thing I

am to you, oh, I pray that you will know.

Awesome God

Rich Mullins

Verses

1. When he rolls up his sleeves, he ain't just
2. And when the sky____ was star - less in the

1. "put-tin' on the ritz." Our God is an awe - some God! There is thun-
2. void___ of the night, Our God is an awe - some God! he spoke in -

1. - der in his foot-steps and light - ning in his fist. Our
2. - to the dark-ness and cre - at - ed the light. Our

1. God is an awe-some God! And the Lord___ was - n't jok-in' when he
2. God is an awe-some God! The judg-ment and wrath__ he___ poured___

1. kicked 'em out of E - den; it was-n't for no rea-son that he
2. ___ out___ on Sod-om, the mer-cy and grace___ he gave us

1. shed his blood. His re - turn is ver - y close and so you
2. at the cross. I hope that we have___ not___ too___

1. bet - ter be be - liev - in' that our God is an awe-some God!
2. ___ quick-ly for - got-ten that our God is an awe-some God!

Our

God is an awe-some God; he reigns from heav'n a-bove with

wis-dom, pow'r and love. Our God is an awe-some God! Our

1, 3

2

to Verse 2

God is an awe-some God!

Final

God is an awe-some God! Our God is an awe-some

God! Our God is an awe-some God!

86

Be Lifted High

Josh Blakesley and Matt Maher

Verses

1. Your voice is over the water. Your voice is
____The heav-ens thun-der your glo - ry. The heav-ens
2. You have made us your cho - sen. You have
 *You have made...

1. o - ver the seas. Your voice is might-y in pow -
____tes - ti - fy. The heav-ens shine in the dark -
2. set us a - part. You have poured out your spir -

1, 3 to Verses

1. - er and wis - dom and love____and__ char - i - ty.
____- ness for all of the na - tions a ho - ly light.
2. - it and start - ed a fire_____with-in our hearts.

2, 4 Refrain

And you will be ex - alt - ed. And you will be

lift - ed high. And you will be our sav -

- ior for-ev - er and ev - er. Our God be glo - ri - fied.

1 to Verse 2

2, 3 1: to Bridge and Coda
2: to Coda ⊕

Bridge

Can I get an "A - men!"

*Repeat 1st line of Verse 2.

Can I get a wit-ness! Can I get an "A-men!"

Can I get a wit-ness! You will be ex - alt -

- ed! You will be lift - ed high! You will be ex - alt -

- ed! You will be lift - ed high!

Bless the Lord

87

Christopher Walker

Refrain

Bless the Lord, O my soul.

Verses   to Refrain

1. God is kind and mer - ci - ful;
2. Gra - cious in his care for all;
3. God is just in all his ways;
4. Close to those who fear his name;
5. God re - veals his stead-fast love;
6. Ho - li - ness in all his works;

God of Wonders

Steve Hindalong and Marc Byrd

Verses

1. Lord of all cre - a - tion,   of wa - ter, earth and
2. Ear - ly in the morn - ing   I will cel - e - brate the

1. sky,   the heav - ens are your tab - er - na -
2. light.   When I stum - ble in the dark -

1. - cle.   Glo - ry to the Lord on high!
2. - ness,   I will call your name by night.

Refrain 1

God of won - ders be - yond our gal - ax - y, you are ho - ly,

ho - ly. The u - ni - verse de - clares your maj - es - ty.

You are ho - ly, ho - ly, Lord of heav - en and earth,

1. | 4 to Verse 2 | 2

Lord of heav - en and earth.

to the Lord of heav - en and earth.

Bridge

Hal - le - lu - jah,

to the Lord of heav - en and earth.

Hal - le - lu - jah,

to the Lord of heav - en and earth.

Hal - le - lu - jah,

Praise & Worship

Interlude **7** Refrain 2

God of won - ders be - yond our gal - ax -
y, you are ho - ly, ho - ly.
Pre-cious Lord, re - veal your heart to me. Fa-ther, hold me,
hold me. The u - ni-verse de-clares your maj - es -
ty. You are ho - ly, ho - ly, ho - ly,
ho - ly! Hal-le-lu - jah, to the
Lord of heav-en and earth. to the
Hal-le-lu - jah,

As needed
Lord of heav-en and earth.
Final
Lord of heav-en and earth.

Praise & Worship

89 God with Us

Sarah Hart and Jayme Thompson

Verses

1. You are high - er than all of our ques-tions,
2. You are strong-er than all of our bur - dens,
3. You bring joy in - to all of our sad - ness,

1. you are deep-er than all of our needs,
2. you are sweet-er than all of our dreams,
3. you bring peace in - to all of our pain,

1. wid - er than all that we can im - ag - ine;
2. clos - er than all the air that sur-rounds us;
3. shin - ing light in - to all of our dark - ness;

1. you are great-er than an - y - thing;
2. you are great-er than an - y - thing.
3. you are great-er than an - y - thing.

[1] to Verse 2 *[2, 3] Refrain*

You are ho - ly, Ho -

ly God Al - might-y, God with us. You are

ho - ly, Ho - ly God Al - might-y,

1, Final — to Verse 3 *[2]*

God with us. God with us.

Bridge

Ev - er be-fore us and ev - er be-side us,

ev - er a-bove us and ev - er be-hind us,

ev - er a-round us and ev - er with-in us, and

6 to Refrain

al - ways God with us.

90   Forever

Chris Tomlin

Praise & Worship

Great God

Dave Wilding

Verse 1
1. You de-liv-er me from all e - vil. You show me your
1. righ - teous-ness. You save me from all dark-
1. - ness. Oh, and you bring your truth and light.

Refrain
My God is a great God. My God is a great God.
My God is a great God. He's a great God.

Verse 2
2. In your house are man-y strang-ers. At your door,
2. you heal the sick. And you said, "Bless-ed are the poor in
to Refrain
2. spir - it," oh, "for they shall be made new." Yeah!

Verse 3
3. Who is there in all the earth in whom I
3. can put my trust? Who can move these might-y moun-
to Refrain
3. - tains? Whose voice can calm these an - gry seas? Yeah!

Praise & Worship

Here I Am

Tom Booth

Refrain

Here I am, stand-ing right be-side you. Here I am;

do not be a - fraid. Here I am, wait-ing like a lov - er.

1-3 to Vss. **Final**

I am here; here I am. am. I am here; here I am.

Verse 1

1. Do not fear when the tempt - er calls you. Do not

1. fear e - ven though you fall. Do not fear, I have con - quered

to Refrain

1. e - vil. Do not fear, nev - er be a - fraid.

Verse 2

2. I am here in the face of ev - 'ry child.

2. I am here in ev - 'ry warm em - brace. I am here with

to Refrain

2. ten - der - ness and mer - cy. Here I am, I am here.

Verse 3

3. I am here in the midst of ev-'ry tri-al. I am

3. here in the face of de-spair. I am here when

to Refrain

3. par-don-ing your broth-er. Here I am, I am here.

93 Here I Am to Worship

Tim Hughes

Verses

1. Light of the world, you stepped down in-to dark-ness, o-pened my eyes,
2. King of all days, oh so high-ly ex-alt-ed, glo-rious in heav-

1. let me see. Beau-ty that made ___ this heart ___ a-dore you,
2. en a-bove. Hum-bly you came to the earth you cre-at-ed,

1. hope of a life spent with you.
2. all for love's sake be-came poor.

Refrain

Here I am to wor-ship, here I am to bow down, here I am to say that you're my God.

You're al-to-geth-er love-ly, al-to-geth-er wor-thy, al-to-geth-er

1, Final (to Verse 2) *(Fine)* **2 Bridge**

won-der-ful to me. And I'll nev-

-er know how much it cost to see my sin up-on

that cross. I'll nev-er know how much it cost to see

my sin up-on that cross. I'll nev-er know how much

it cost to see my sin up-on that cross.

I'll nev - er know how much it cost to see

to Refrain

my sin up - on that cross.

94

He Is Exalted

Twila Paris

Refrain

He is ex-alt-ed, the King is ex-alt-ed on high; I will
praise him. He is ex-alt-ed, for-ev-er ex-alt-ed and
I will praise his name!
He is the Lord; for-ev-er his truth shall
reign. Heav-en and earth re-
joice in his ho-ly name. He is ex-alt-ed, the

1. King is ex-alt-ed on high!   to Refrain

2. high!   Final   high!

He is ex-alt-ed, the King is ex-alt-ed on high!

*Sing cue notes after the first time.

Holy God, We Praise Thy Name

GROSSER GOTT

1. Ho - ly God, we praise thy name; Lord of all, we
2. Hark! the loud ce - les - tial hymn An - gel choirs a -
3. Lo! the ap - os - tol - ic train Join, the sa - cred
4. Ho - ly Fa - ther, Ho - ly Son, Ho - ly Spir - it,

1. bow be - fore thee! All on earth thy scep - tre claim,
2. bove are rais - ing; Cher - u - bim and Ser - a - phim,
3. Name to hal - low; Proph - ets swell the loud re - frain,
4. Three we name thee; While in es - sence on - ly One,

1. All in heav'n a - bove a - dore thee; In - fi -
2. In un - ceas - ing cho - rus prais-ing; Fill the
3. And the white - robed mar - tyrs fol - low; And from
4. Un - di - vid - ed God we claim thee; And a -

1. nite, thy vast do - main, Ev - er - last - ing
2. heav'ns with sweet ac - cord: "Ho - ly, ho - ly,
3. morn to set of sun, Through the Church the
4. dor - ing, bend the knee, While we own the

1. is thy reign. In - fi - nite, thy vast do -
2. ho - ly Lord!" Fill the heav'ns with sweet ac -
3. song goes on. And from morn to set of
4. mys - ter - y. And a - dor - ing, bend the

1. main, Ev - er - last - ing is thy reign.
2. cord: "Ho - ly, ho - ly, ho - ly Lord!"
3. sun, Through the Church the song goes on.
4. knee, While we own the mys - ter - y.

Text: 78 78 77 with repeat; Te Deum laudamus; attr. to St. Nicetas, ca. 335–414; Grosser Gott, wir loben dich; tr. ascr. to Ignaz Franz, 1719–1790; tr. by Clarence A. Walworth, 1820–1900. Music: Allgemeines Katholisches Gesangbuch, Vienna, ca. 1774.

Praise & Worship

I Can Only Imagine

Bart Millard

Verse 1
1. I can on-ly i-mag-ine what it will be like

1. when I walk by your side. I can on-ly i-mag-ine

1. what my eyes will see when your face is be-fore me.

1. I can on-ly i-mag-ine. Sur-

Refrain
round-ed by your glo-ry, what will my heart feel?

Will I dance for you, Je-sus, or in awe of you be still?

Will I stand in your pres-ence or to my knees will I fall?

Will I sing hal-le-lu-jah? Will I be a-ble to speak at all?

to Coda
I can on-ly i-mag-ine. I can on-ly i-mag-ine.

Verse 2

2. I can on-ly i-mag-ine   when that day   comes

2. and I find   my-self   stand-ing in   the Son.

2. I can on-ly i-mag-ine   when all I   will do

2. is for-ev-er,   for-ev-er wor-ship you.   I can on-ly i-

2. mag-ine,   I can on-ly i-mag-ine.   Sur-

Coda

I can on-ly i-mag-ine.

I can on-ly i-mag-ine   when all I   will do

is for-ev-er,   for-ev-er wor-ship you.

I can on-ly i-mag-ine.

97 I Could Sing of Your Love Forever

Martin Smith

Bridge

Oh, I feel like danc - ing;

it's fool-ish-ness I know.

But when the world has seen the light,

they will dance with joy like we're danc -

4   to Refrain

- ing now.

How Great Is Your Name

Cyprian Consiglio

Refrain

How great is your name, great is your name, how great is your name through all the earth! How great is your name, great is your name, how great is your name through all the earth!

1. Your majesty is praised above the heavens,

Response A

great is your name, great is your name!

On the lips of all the children and the babies,

Response B

Great is your name through all the earth!

You've found praise
to foil all your enemies,
(Response A)
To silence ev'ry foe and ev'ry rebel.
(Response B)

2. When I see the heavens,
the work of your fingers,
(Response A)
The moon and all the stars,
how you arranged them,
(Response B)
Lord, who are we
that you should even bother?
(Response A)
Mere mortal ones
that you could even care for us?
(Response B)

3. Yet you made us little less than the angels,
(Response A)
With majesty and honor you crowned us!
(Response B)
Gave us power over all of creation,
(Response A)
By putting all things under our dominion!
(Response B)

4. All your creatures, the sheep and the cattle,
(Response A)
The savage beasts that roam in the forest,
(Response B)
The birds that make their way
through the heavens,
(Response A)
And the fish that make their way
through the water.
(Response B)

I Will Lift Up Your Name

Steve Angrisano and Tom Tomaszek

Refrain
I will lift up your name: praise to my king and God, for you are ho - ly. Oh, I will lift up your name: praise to my king and my God on high!

Last time
I will lift up your name: praise to my king and my God on high!

Verses
1. I will give you glo - ry, Lord; I will bless your
2. Al-ways faith - ful, kind and gen-tle, slow to an - ger,
3. Ev - 'ry crea - ture, great and small, tells the glo - ry

1. name for - ev - er. I will praise you day af - ter
2. filled with love. Oh, how great is the Lord of
3. of your name, and pro-claims to all your might - y

1, 2 *to Refrain* | 3 | 4 *to Refrain*
1. day.
2. all!
3. ways.

100 Just Like You

Matt Maher

Verses

1. Re-vive my heart, re - new my soul.__ In you, O Lord, I
2. Oh, lift me up, God, my Fa-ther. In all this world there

1. am made whole.__ No more in fear will I
2. is no oth - er. I'm danc - ing in your ho - ly

1. wan - der, 'cause you're my God, my Lord and lov - er.
2. pres-ence, and your glo - ry fills_____ all my sens - es.

1-2. Like a burn-ing fire be my one de - sire.

Refrain

I want to be ho - ly just like you. I want to go where

you lead me to. With reck-less a-ban - don to your truth,

1-2 to Vs 2/to Refrain

I want to fall deep - er in love with you.

Final

and deep - er and deep - er and deep-er and deep - er in love with you,

and deep - er and deep - er and deep - er and deep - er in love with

3 Sing 3 times

you. I want to be ho -

ly. I want to be ho - ly.

Praise & Worship

Lord, I Lift Your Name on High

101

Rick Founds

Lord, I lift your name on high. Lord, I
I'm so glad you're in my life. I'm so

love to sing your prais - es.
glad you came to save us.

You came from heav - en to earth to show the way.

From the earth to the cross, my debt to pay.

From the cross to the grave, from the grave to the sky;

Lord, I lift your name on high.

Final
sing 3 times

high. Lord, I lift your name on high.

102 Open the Eyes of My Heart

Paul Baloche

O - pen the eyes of my heart, Lord, o - pen the eyes

of my heart. I want to see you.

I want to see you.

Verse

To see you high and lift - ed up,

shin - ing in the light of your glo - ry.

Pour out your pow'r and love as we sing

"Ho - ly, ho - ly, ho - ly."

- ly." - ly."

Final Refrain

*Melody 1

1. Ho - ly, ho - ly, ho - ly, ho - ly, ho -

*Melody 2

2. O - pen the eyes of my heart, Lord. O - pen the eyes

1. - ly, ho - ly, ho - ly, ho - ly, ho -

2. of my heart. I want to see you.

repeat as needed

1. - ly, I want to see you.

repeat as needed

2. I want to see you.

*Melodies 1 and 2 may be sung separately or together, as desired.

103

Our God Is Good

Joshua Blakesley and Cooper Ray

Refrain

Our God is good, our God is good, ho-ly and righ-teous, pow-er-ful and true. _(Fine)_

Verses

1. Bless-ed be God who lives for-ev-er
2. Let all ___ peo-ple speak of his great-ness

1. be-cause his king-dom lives on and on and on.
2. be-cause he is our Sav-ior and our king.

1. Lift your ___ voic-es, sing
2. Re-joice in the good things he

1. his prais-es; ex-
2. has done ___ for you; give

to Refrain

1. alt him in the sight of ev-'ry-one.
2. thanks and praise for all the joy he brings.

Bridge

I ex-alt my God and my soul re-joic - es in him,

the Lord of heav - en. The

ends of the earth will shout songs of praise and

all the peo - ple will sing, they will

3 to Refrain

sing:

Rejoice in the Lord/Alégrense Todos

Santiago Fernández

Estrofas/Verses

1. Nos a-le-gra-mos en ti, buen Je-sús, tú nues-tro
2. A-sí que-re-mos vi-vir, buen Se-ñor, ha-cien-do

1. go-zo y tú nues-tra luz. *With will-ing spir-its we*
2. to-do con gus-to y a-mor. *Give us the cour-age to*

1. an-swer the call to live in joy as we re-call
2. live out the call

1, 2. your great com-mand in the words of Paul:

Estribillo/Refrain

Re-joice in the Lord! ¡A-lé-gren-se to-dos!

1, 3

Re-pi-to: Es-tén a-le-gres. ¡Cer-ca es-tá el Se-ñor!

2 a la Estrofa 2/ to Verse 2

8

Give love and kind-ness and you'll have the peace of God.

Final

Give love and kind-ness and you'll have the peace of God.

Text: Based on Philippians 4:4–8. Text and music © 2006, Santiago Fernández.
Published by spiritandsong.com®, a division of OCP. All rights reserved.

Shine, Jesus, Shine

Graham Kendrick

Refrain

Shine, Je-sus, shine; fill this land with the Fa-ther's glo-ry.
Blaze, Spir-it, blaze; set our hearts on fire. Flow, riv-er, flow;
flood the na-tions with grace and mer-cy. Send forth your Word,

1-3, Final | *4*
to Verses | to Refrain

Lord, and let there be light. light.

Verses

1. Lord, the light of your love is shin-ing, in the midst of the
2. Lord, I come to your awe-some pres-ence, from the shad-ows in-
3. As we gaze on your king-ly bright-ness, so our fac-es dis-

1. dark-ness, shin-ing. Je-sus, Light of the world, shine up-
2. to your ra-diance. By the blood I may en-ter your
3. play your like-ness, ev-er chang-ing from glo-ry to

1. on us. Set us free by the truth you now bring us.
2. bright-ness. Search me, try me, con-sume all my dark-ness.
3. glo-ry. Mir-rored here, may our lives tell your sto-ry.

to Refrain

1-3. Shine on me, shine on me.

106   Shout to the Lord

Darlene Zschech

My Je-sus, my Sav-ior; Lord, there is none like you.

All of my days I want to praise

the won-ders of your might - y love. My com-fort,

my shel-ter, tow-er of ref - uge and strength; let ev-'ry breath,

all that I am, nev-er cease to wor - ship you.

Refrain

Shout to the Lord, all the earth; Let us sing

pow-er and maj - es - ty, praise to the King.

Moun-tains bow down and the seas will roar at the sound

of your name. I sing for joy at the work

of your hands. For - ev - er I'll love you, for - ev -

- er I'll stand. Noth-ing com - pares to the prom-

3   to Verse

- ise I have in you.

Praise & Worship

The Lord Has Done Great Things

107

Jaime Cortez

Refrain: 1st time: Cantor, All repeat; thereafter: All

The Lord has done great things for us, we are filled with glad - ness and joy, we are filled with glad - ness and joy.

Verse 1: Cantor/Choir

1. When God set the cap-tives of Zi - on free, we were more like
1. chil-dren in a dream. Then you could hear our laugh - ter and
1. cheers; then you could hear our shouts of joy.

to Refrain

Verses 2, 3: Cantor/Choir

2. They said in a - maze-ment to the world, "In-deed, God has
3. Re - store all our for - tunes, God of love, like riv - ers that
2. done great things for them." Tru - ly our God has done
3. save the des - ert lands. Those who have gone to sow
2. great things, and so we are glad, we shout for joy.
3. in tears shall go back to reap with songs of joy.

to Refrain

Text: Psalm 126:1-2, 2-3, 4-5. Refrain text © 1969, 1981, ICEL. All rights reserved. Used with permission.
Music and verses text © 1995, Jaime Cortez. Published by OCP. All rights reserved.

108 Sometimes by Step

Rich Mullins and Beaker

Verses

1. Some-times the night is beau - ti - ful.
2. Some-times I think of A - bra - ham, how

1. Some-times the sky_____ was so far a - way.
2. one star he saw____ had been lit for him.____

1. Some-times it seems to be so close you could touch
2. He was a strang - er in this land. And I am

1. it, but your heart would break. Some-times the morn -
2. that, no____ less than he, and on the road

1. - ing came too soon. Some - times the day
2. to righ - teous - ness. Some - times the climb

1. could be so hard. There was so much work left
2. can be so steep I may fal - ter in

1. to do, but so much you'd al - read - y done.
2. my steps, and nev - er be - yond____ your reach.

Refrain

O God, you are my God, and I will ev-er praise

you. O God, you are my God, and

I will ev-er praise you. And I will seek you in the morn-

-ing and I will learn to walk in your ways. And

step by step you'll lead me, and I will fol-low you all of my

1
days.

to Verse 2

2
days. And I will fol-low you all of my

days. And I will fol-low you all of my days.

And step by step you'll lead me, and I will

(Fine)   Repeat ad lib.

fol-low you all of my days.   And I will

109   That Where I Am

Rich Mullins

Verse 1

1. In my Fa-ther's house there are man-y, man-y rooms. In my

1. Fa-ther's house there are man-y, man-y rooms. And I'm

1. go-ing up there now to pre-pare a place for you, that where I am

1. there you may al-so be.

Verse 2

2. If I go pre-pare a place for you, I will come back a-gain.

2. If I go pre-pare a place for you, I

2. will come back a-gain. You know I am the Way, the Truth, the Life.

2. Keep my com-mand, that where I am, there you may al-so be.

Refrain

That where I am, there you may al-so be, up where the

truth, the truth will set you free. In the world,

you will have trou-ble, but I leave you my peace, that where I

1
2   to Verse 3
2, Final   to Refrain

am, there you may al - so be. be.

Verse 3

3. Re-mem - ber, you did not choose me; no, I have cho-sen you. Re-

3. mem - ber, you did not choose me; no, I have cho-sen you. The world

3. will show you ha-tred, the Spir-it show you truth, that where I

2

3. am, there you may al - so be.

Verse 4

4. I've come down from the Fa - ther, time for me to go back

4. up. Oh, I've come down from the Fa - ther, time for me

4. to go back up. One com-mand I leave you: love as I have

to Refrain

4. loved, that where I am, there you may al - so be.

Praise & Worship

110   Trading My Sorrows

Darrell Evans

I'm trad-ing my sor-rows, I'm trad-ing my shame;

I'm lay-ing them down for the joy of the Lord.

I'm trad-ing my sick-ness, I'm trad-ing my

pain; I'm lay-ing them down for the joy of the Lord.

Refrain

We say yes, Lord, yes, Lord, yes, yes, Lord,

yes, Lord, yes, Lord, yes, yes, Lord, yes, Lord, yes, Lord,

1... | 1st time: to Verse / 2nd time: to Bridge / 3rd time: to Coda | Final

yes, yes, Lord. A-men.   yes, yes, Lord. A-men.

Bridge

I am pressed but not crushed, per-se-cut-ed, not a-

ban-doned, struck down but not de-stroyed. I am blessed

be-yond the curse, for his prom-ise will en-dure, that his

joy is gon-na be my strength. Though the sor-row may

last for   the night, his joy   comes with the morn-ing.

Coda

La la la   la la la   la la la la la   la

la   la   la la   la   la la la   la la   la

1st time: repeat
2nd time: to Refrain

la la   la la la   la la la   la la la la.

111   We Ever Will Praise You

Angus McDonell

Refrain

We ev-er will praise you; we ev-er will sing
sweet psalms of joy to you, our king.
O Mak-er of heav - en, of earth and the sea,
sweet psalms of joy we ev-er will sing.

Verses

1. Hap - py are those whose help - er
2. Bless - ed are those whose hope is

1. is _____ the Lord who ev - er was and
2. in the Lord; _____ the low - ly shall be raised, the

1. ev - er - more shall be. All who are blind,
2. fa - ther - less sus - tained. Loved are the ones

1. well, they shall see, _____ the
2. who live in righ - teous-ness, _____ the

1. pris - on - ers set _____ free, the hun-gry, they shall
2. wid-owed and the or - phaned, they are not for -

to Refrain

1. eat. _____
2. sak - en. _____

we ev-er will sing. We ev-er will

praise your name. We ev-er will praise your name.

We ev-er will praise your name.

Text: Based on Psalm 146. Text and music © 1997, Angus McDonell. Published by spiritandsong.com®, a division of OCP. All rights reserved.

112 Your Grace Is Enough

Matt Maher

Verses

1. Great is your faith - ful - ness, O God of Ja - cob;
2. Great is your love and jus - tice, God of Ja - cob;

1. you wres - tle with the sin - ner's rest -
2. you use the weak to lead the strong.

1. - less heart.   You lead me by
2.   You lead us in

1. still wa - ters in - to mer - cy
2. the song of heav - en's vic - t'ry,

1. where noth - ing can keep us a - part.
2. and all your peo - ple sing a - long.

Bridge

So re - mem - ber your peo - ple, re -

mem - ber your chil - dren, re - mem - ber your

prom - ise, O God.

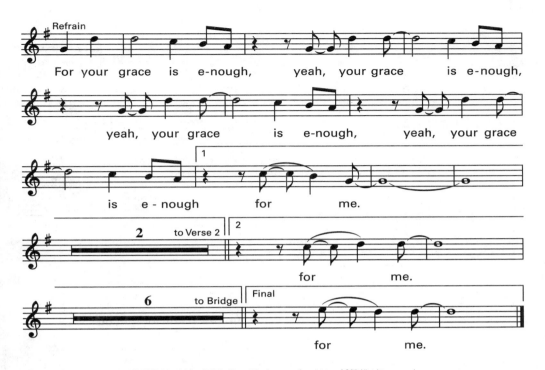

For your grace is e-nough, yeah, your grace is e-nough,

yeah, your grace is e-nough, yeah, your grace

is e-nough for me.

to Verse 2 for me.

to Bridge | Final for me.

113 Breathe

Marie Barnett

Verse

This is the air I breathe. This is the air
This is my dai - ly bread. This is my dai-

I breathe. Your ho - ly pres - ence
- ly bread. Your ver - y word

1 | liv - ing in me.
spo - ken to me. | 2

Refrain
And I, I'm des-p'rate for you.

And I, I'm lost with-out

As needed to beginning | Final
you. I'm lost with-out

repeat as needed
you. I'm lost with-out you.

This is the air I breathe.

This is the air I breathe.

Father, I Adore You

114

Terrye Coelho

Round

1. Fa - ther,
2. Je - sus, } I a-dore you. Lay my life be - fore you. How I love you.
3. Spir - it,

I Shall Not Want

115

Tom Booth

Refrain *Fine*

The Lord is my shep-herd, I shall not want.

Verse 1

1. When the day is long and temp - ta - tion strong and the

1. cords of death en-com-pass me, I cry out in need of de-

to Refrain

1. liv - er - ance. You take my hand and give me rest.

Verse 2

2. E-ven though I walk in the dark of night, I fear not,

2. for you are God. And you care for me like the

to Refrain

2. spar - row. At my side you give me strength.

116   How Can I Keep from Singing

ENDLESS SONG

Verses

1. My life flows on in end - less song; A-
2. Through all the tu - mult and the strife, I
3. What though the tem - pest 'round me roar, I
4. When ty - rants trem - ble, sick with fear, And
5. The peace of Christ makes fresh my heart, A

1. bove earth's lam - en - ta - tion. I hear the real though
2. hear that mu - sic ring - ing; It sounds and ech - oes
3. hear the truth it liv - eth. What though the dark - ness
4. hear their death knells ring - ing; When friends re - joice both
5. foun - tain ev - er spring - ing. All things are mine since

1. far - off hymn That hails a new cre - a - tion.
2. in my soul; How can I keep from sing - ing?
3. 'round me close, Songs in the night it giv - eth.
4. far and near, How can I keep from sing - ing?
5. I am his; How can I keep from sing - ing?

Refrain

No storm can shake my in-most calm, While to that rock I'm

cling-ing. Since Love is Lord of heav-en and earth,

How can I keep from sing-ing?

Text: 87 87 with refrain; attr. to Robert Lowry, 1826–1899, alt.; verse 3, Doris Plenn. Music: Quaker Hymn; attr. to Robert Lowry.

Prayer & Devotion

Thy Word Is a Lamp

Michael W. Smith

Prayer & Devotion

118   Jesus, Come to Us

David Haas

Refrain

Je - sus, come to us, lead us to your light. Je - sus, be with us,

for we need you.

Verses

1. Lord, we come be - fore you,_____ lis - ten
2. Lord, we come to praise you for your faith - ful -
3. Lord, you give us won - ders, __ your glo -

to Refrain

1. to our prayer. Fill us all with hope and your love.
2. ness through night. You will be with us, this we know.
3. ry to all. We be - lieve in you, come to us.

119   Jesus, I Trust in You

Angus McDonell and Sarah Hart

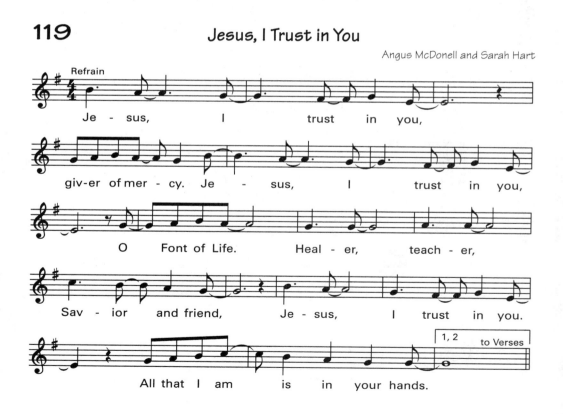

Refrain

Je - sus, I trust in you,

giv - er of mer - cy. Je - sus, I trust in you,

O Font of Life. Heal - er, teach - er,

Sav - ior and friend, Je - sus, I trust in you.

1, 2
to Verses

All that I am is in your hands.

Final

All that I am is in your hands.

Verses

1. Let not this heart be trou - bled, but
2. As you gave up your - self, Lord, in -

1. let it rest in you. For with you,
2. to your Fa - ther's hands, so let me

1. ev - 'ry sor - row will be washed a - way. Let
2. give my - self to all that is your will. And

1. not my mind be bur - dened, but
2. as you emp - tied your - self, ful -

1. set it free with truth, for ev - 'ry care is lost
2. filled Love's per - fect plan, let me be emp - tied, that

to Refrain

1. in un - der - stand - ing grace.
2. my life might be ful - filled.

Text © 2003, Sarah Hart. Music © 2003, Angus McDonell and Sarah Hart. Published by spiritandsong.com®, a division of OCP. All rights reserved.

120   My Soul Is Thirsting/As Morning Breaks

Steve Angrisano

*Alternative refrain text.

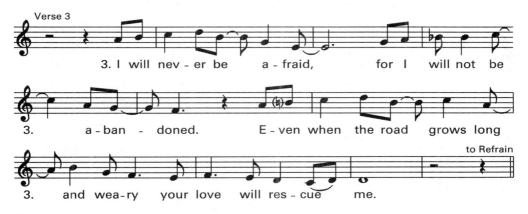

Verse 3

3. I will nev-er be a-fraid, for I will not be
3. a-ban-doned. E-ven when the road grows long
   to Refrain
3. and wea-ry your love will res-cue me.

Lord of All Hopefulness

121

SLANE

1. Lord of all hope-ful-ness, Lord of all joy, Whose
2. Lord of all ea-ger-ness, Lord of all faith, Whose
3. Lord of all kind-li-ness, Lord of all grace, Your
4. Lord of all gen-tle-ness, Lord of all calm, Whose

1. trust, ev-er child-like, no cares can de-stroy, Be
2. strong hands were skilled at the plane and the lathe, Be
3. hands swift to wel-come, your arms to em-brace, Be
4. voice is con-tent-ment, whose pres-ence is balm, Be

1. there at our wak-ing, and give us, we pray, Your
2. there at our la-bors, and give us, we pray, Your
3. there at our hom-ing, and give us, we pray, Your
4. there at our sleep-ing, and give us, we pray, Your

1. bliss in our hearts, Lord, at the break of the day.
2. strength in our hearts, Lord, at the noon of the day.
3. love in our hearts, Lord, at the eve of the day.
4. peace in our hearts, Lord, at the end of the day.

122

Open My Eyes/Abre Mis Ojos

Jesse Manibusan

Verses

1, 5. O - pen my__ eyes,_____ Lord. Help me to
2. O - pen my__ ears,_____ Lord. Help me to
3. O - pen my__ heart,_____ Lord. Help me to
4. I live with - in_____ you. Deep in your

1, 5. A - bre mis__ o - jos, que quie - ro
2. A - bre mis o - í - dos, que quie-ro o -
3. A - bre mi__ co - ra - zón, que quie-ro a -
4. Ven y des - can - sa en__ mi

1, 5. see your__ face. O - pen my__ eyes,__ Lord._____
2. hear your__ voice. O - pen my__ ears,__ Lord._____
3. love like__ you. O - pen my__ heart,__ Lord._____
4. heart, O____ Love. I live with - in____ you.____

1, 5. ver co - mo tú. A - bre mis__ o - jos,_____ a -
2. ír co - mo tú. A - bre mis o - í - dos,_____ a -
3. mar co - mo tú. A - bre mi__ co - ra-zón,_____ a -
4. co - ra - zón. Ven y des - can - sa,_____

1, 2, 4 | **3** to Bridge | **Final**

1, 5. Help me to see. 3. love. 5. see.
2. Help me to hear. mar. ver.
3. Help me to
4. Rest now in me.

1, 5. yú - da-me a ver.
2. yú - da-me a o - ír.
3. yú - da-me a a -
4. te a - li - via - ré.

Prayer & Devotion

Bridge

And the first___ shall be last,___ and our eyes are
Da - me la a-le-grí - a de tu sal - va -

___o - pened, and we'll hear like nev-er be - fore.___ And we'll
ción,___ cre-a en mí un co-ra - zón pu - ro.___ No me a-

speak in___ new ways,___ and we'll see God's___ face in___
rro - jes___ le - jos de tu ros - tro, Se - ñor, no me

to Verse 4

plac - es___ we've nev-er known.___
qui - tes tu san - to es - pí - ri - tu.___

123

To You, O God, I Lift Up My Soul

Bob Hurd

Refrain: 1st time: Cantor, All repeat; thereafter: All

To you, O God, I lift up my soul; lift up my spir-it

to my Lord. To you I lift up my soul.

To you I lift up my soul. To you I lift up my soul.

Verses: Cantor

1. Make me to know your ways, O God; teach me your
2. Good and up-right our gra - cious God, show-ing the
3. Stead-fast and kind your ways, O God; all who re-

to Refrain

1. paths, guide me. ‹ You are my Sav - ior.
2. way, guid - ing the hum-ble to jus - tice.
3. vere your cov - e - nant ‹ know your friend-ship.

See, I Make All Things New

124

Tom Booth

Refrain

"See, I make all things new," says the Lord, your God.

"See, I make all things new. Yes, e - ven you."

Final

Yes, e - ven you. Yes, e - ven you."

Verses

1. I will raise you up on wings of an ea - gle
2. You are to be a light to shine a - mong the na - tions
3. Come un - to me all you heav - i - ly lad - en

1. and I will see you through. For I am your
2. and I will see you through. For I am your
3. and I will see you through. For I am your

to Refrain

1. Lord and God; I am the way.
2. por - tion and cup; I am the truth.
3. sav - ing help; I am the life.

125 Enter the Journey/Sigue el Camino

Mark Friedman and Janet Vogt

Refrain

En - ter the jour - ney.___ Come to the song. By God
Si - gue_el ca - mi - no de la sal - va - ción. Es Dios

you are cho-sen, by name you are called to fol - low the vi -
quien te lla - ma, es - cu - cha su voz:___ Si - gue_el ca - mi -

- sion, car - ry the cross. En - ter the jour - ney of
- no, car - ga la cruz. Jun - tos en la mis - ma

*

faith as the fam - 'ly of God.
fe, co - mo fa - mi - lia de Dios.

Verses

All   **Cantor/Choir**

1. En - ter the jour - ney, the___ way may be long.___
2. En - ter the jour - ney, though___ lost and un - sure.___
3. En - ter the jour - ney, though___ dark is the way.___
4. En - ter the jour - ney, the___ old and the young.___
1. Si - gue_el ca - mi - no, sea___ lar - go, sea du - ro.
2. Si - gue_el ca - mi - no, no te sien - tas per - di - do.
3. Si - gue_el ca - mi - no, en___ la_obs - cu - ri - dad.___
4. Si - gue_el ca - mi - no, seas___ jo - ven o_an - cia - no.

All   **Cantor/Choir**

1. En - ter the jour - ney, yet___ we are made strong.___
2. En - ter the jour - ney, God's___ peace will be yours.___
3. En - ter the jour - ney, do___ not be a - fraid,___
4. En - ter the jour - ney, the___ king - dom is won.___
1. Si - gue_el ca - mi - no, aun-que_es - tés in - se - gu - ro.
2. Si - gue_el ca - mi - no, por - que Dios ha ven - ci - do.
3. Si - gue_el ca - mi - no, que___ so - lo no_es - tás.___
4. Si - gue_el ca - mi - no, que_hay vic - to - ria_en el rei - no.

*Last time, repeat final phrase.

Opening of the School Year

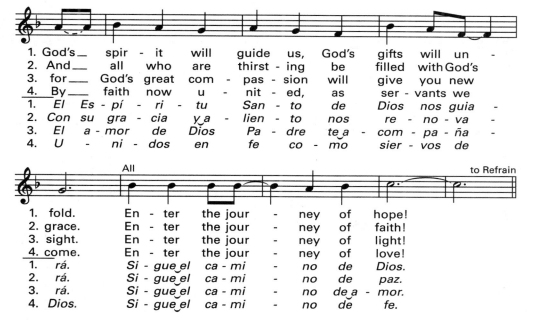

1. God's___ spir - it will guide us, God's gifts will un -
2. And___ all who are thirst - ing be filled with God's
3. for___ God's great com - pas - sion will give you new
4. By___ faith now u - nit - ed, as ser - vants we

1. El Es - pí - ri - tu San - to de Dios nos guia -
2. Con su gra - cia y a - lien - to nos re - no - va -
3. El a - mor de Dios Pa - dre te a - com - pa - ña -
4. U - ni - dos en fe co - mo sier - vos de

All   to Refrain

1. fold.   En - ter the jour - ney of hope!
2. grace.   En - ter the jour - ney of faith!
3. sight.   En - ter the jour - ney of light!
4. come.   En - ter the jour - ney of love!

1. rá.   Si - gue el ca - mi - no de Dios
2. rá.   Si - gue el ca - mi - no de paz.
3. rá.   Si - gue el ca - mi - no de a - mor.
4. Dios.   Si - gue el ca - mi - no de fe.

English text: Mark Friedman and Janet Vogt; Spanish text: Estela García, Pedro Rubalcava and Rodolfo López.
Text and music © 2000, 2002, Mark Friedman and Janet Vogt. Published by OCP. All rights reserved.

Opening of the School Year

126
We Will Walk

Tom Booth

Refrain

And we will walk in the pres-ence of the Lord in the land of the liv - ing. And we will dance in the pres-ence of the Lord in the land of the liv - ing.

Verses

1. Praise the Lord,_____ all you ser-vants of the Lord;
2. A - bove all na - tions is the king-dom of the Lord,

1. praise his name__ who is on____ high.
2. a - bove the_____ heav - ens is his glo - ry;

1. From the ris - ing to the set-ting of the sun
2. en-throned on high,___ who is like our God,

1
1. should the Lord, our God, be praised.

to Refrain *2*
2. look-ing on the earth be -

Final Refrain

low? And we will walk in the pres-ence of the Lord in the land of the liv - ing. And we will laugh in the pres-ence of the Lord in the land of the liv - ing.

Opening of the School Year

God Has Chosen Me

127

Bernadette Farrell

Verses

1. God has cho-sen me, God has cho-sen me to bring good news
2. God has cho-sen me, God has cho-sen me to set a - light
3. God is call-ing me, God is call-ing me in all whose cry

1. to the poor. God has cho-sen me, God has cho-sen me to
2. a new fire. God has cho-sen me, God has cho-sen me to
3. is un-heard. God is call-ing me, God is call-ing me to

1. bring new sight to those search-ing for light: God has
2. bring to birth a new king-dom on earth: God has
3. raise up the voice with no pow-er or choice: God is

Refrain

1. cho - sen me, cho - sen me: And to tell the world
2. cho - sen me, cho - sen me:
3. call - ing me, call - ing me:

that God's king-dom is near, to re-move op-pres - sion and

break down fear, yes, God's time is near, God's time is near,

God's time is near, God's time is near.

Catechetical Sunday

Fish with Me

Ken Canedo

Verse 1

1. Je - sus saw them fish-ing by the shore of Gal - i - lee,

1. cast - ing out their nets in - to the sea.

1. Si - mon Pe - ter, An - drew and the sons

1. of Zeb - e - dee, wait - ing in their

1. boats so pa - tient - ly. And Je - sus said,

Refrain

"Oh, come and fol - low me.

Oh, leave be - hind your nets. I call you.

Oh, come and fish with me, and your

life will nev - er be the same a - gain."

(1: to Vs. 2)
(2: to Bridge)
(Last: to Coda ⊕)

2. A rich young per-son came to Je-sus
2. look-ing for ad-vice. "How can I ob-tain e-ter-nal
2. life?" Je-sus told him, "Hon-or the com-mand-
2. -ments of the Lord. Then sell off all your
2. rich-es for the poor." And Je-sus said,

Bridge
Those who save their lives will lose them. Those who
lose their lives will save them. For what prof-it
does it show if you gain the world but lose your
soul, your soul?

Note: Verse 3 found on next page.

Verse 3

3. "If you want to fol-low me de - ny your ver - y self.

3. Take up your cross and walk the walk with

3. me. This might seem a hard - ship, an im -

3. pos - si - bil - i - ty, but noth-ing is im -

to Refrain

3. pos - si - ble with God." And Je - sus said,

Coda

Yes, your life will nev - er be the same a -

gain. Oh, your life will nev - er be the same.

Text: Based on Matthew 4:18–22; 16:24–26; 19:16–21, 25–26. Text and music © 2002, Ken Canedo.
Published by spiritandsong.com®, a division of OCP. All rights reserved.

Pescador de Hombres/Lord, You Have Come   129

Cesáreo Gabaráin

Estrofas/Verses

1. Tú has ve - ni - do a la o - ri - lla, no has bus - ca - do
2. Tú sa - bes bien lo que ten - go; en mi bar - ca
3. Tú ne - ce - si - tas mis ma - nos, mi can - san - cio
4. Tú, pes - ca - dor de o - tros la - gos, an - sia e - ter - na
1. Lord, you have come to the sea-shore, nei - ther search-ing for
2. Lord, see my goods, my pos - ses - sions; in my boat you find
3. Lord, take my hands and di - rect them. Help me spend my - self
4. Lord, as I drift on the wa - ters, be the rest - ing place

1. ni a sa - bios ni a ri - cos; _____ tan só - lo quie - res
2. no hay o - ro ni es - pa - das, _____ tan só - lo re - des
3. que a o - tros des - can - se, _____ a - mor que quie - ra
4. de al - mas que es - pe - ran, _____ a - mi - go bue - no,
1. the rich nor the wise, _____ de - sir - ing on - ly
2. no pow - er, no wealth. _____ Will you ac - cept, then,
3. in seek-ing the lost, _____ re - turn - ing love for
4. of my rest - less heart, _____ my life's com - pan - ion,

Estribillo/Refrain

1. que yo te si - ga.
2. y mi tra - ba - jo.
3. se - guir a - man - do.
4. que a - sí me lla - mas.
1. that I should fol - low.
2. my nets and la - bor?
3. the love you gave me.
4. my friend and ref - uge.

Se - ñor, me has mi - ra - do a los

O Lord, with your eyes set up-

o - jos, son - ri - en - do _____ has di - cho mi
on me, gent - ly smil - ing, _____ you have spo-ken my

nom - bre, _____ en la a - re - na he de - ja - do mi bar - ca,
name; _____ all I longed for I have found by the wa - ter,

jun - to a ti bus - ca - ré o - tro mar.
at your side, I will seek oth - er shores.

Catechetical Sunday

130 Blest the People/Oh, When the Saints

Blest the People by Craig and Kristen Colson
WHEN THE SAINTS, Spiritual
Adapted by Craig and Kristen Colson

Refrain

Blest the peo - ple the Lord has cho - sen

to be ho - ly in pu - ri - ty.

Verse 1

1a. Ho - ly Ma - ry, Bless - ed Moth - er,
1b. Juan Di - e - go, on the moun - tain,
1c. Saint The - re - sa, Lit - tle Flow - er,

1a. help us say yes,__ just like you.
1b. on your til - ma__ her face ap - peared.
1c. lead us all_____ to pu - ri - ty.

Refrain I

Blest the peo - ple the Lord has cho - sen

to be ho - ly in pu - ri - ty.

Refrain II

Oh, when the saints go march - in' in,

oh, when the saints go march - in' in, oh, I want to be

1: to Verse 2
2: to Refrain II
(Fine)

in that num - ber when the saints go march - in' in.

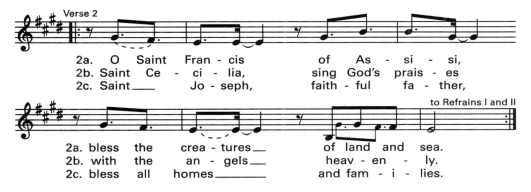

Verse 2

2a. O Saint Fran - cis of As - si - si,
2b. Saint Ce - ci - lia, sing God's prais - es
2c. Saint___ Jo - seph, faith - ful fa - ther,

to Refrains I and II

2a. bless the crea - tures___ of land and sea.
2b. with the an - gels___ heav - en - ly.
2c. bless all homes_____ and fam - i - lies.

For All the Saints   131

SINE NOMINE

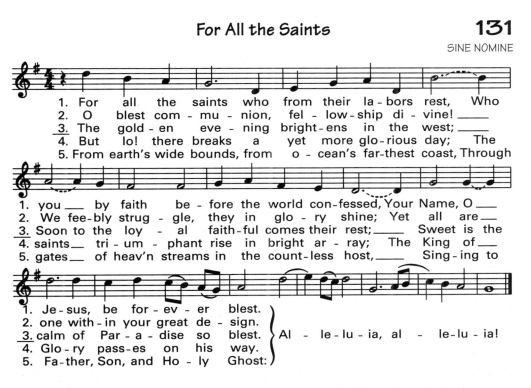

1. For all the saints who from their la - bors rest, Who
2. O blest com - mu - nion, fel - low-ship di - vine!___
3. The gold - en eve - ning bright-ens in the west;___
4. But lo! there breaks a yet more glo - rious day; The
5. From earth's wide bounds, from o - cean's far-thest coast, Through

1. you___ by faith be - fore the world con-fessed, Your Name, O___
2. We fee-bly strug - gle, they in glo - ry shine; Yet all are___
3. Soon to the loy - al faith-ful comes their rest;___ Sweet is the
4. saints___ tri - um - phant rise in bright ar - ray; The King of___
5. gates___ of heav'n streams in the count-less host,___ Sing-ing to

1. Je - sus, be for - ev - er blest. ⎫
2. one with - in your great de - sign. ⎪
3. calm of Par - a - dise so blest. ⎬ Al - le - lu - ia, al - le - lu - ia!
4. Glo - ry pass-es on his way. ⎪
5. Fa - ther, Son, and Ho - ly Ghost: ⎭

Text: 10 10 10 with alleluias; William W. How, 1823–1897, alt. Music: English Hymnal, 1906; Ralph Vaughan Williams, 1872–1958.

132 Because the Lord Is My Shepherd

Christopher Walker

Verses

1. Be - cause ___ the Lord is my shep-herd, I have
2. And when ___ the road leads to dark - ness, I shall
3. In love ___ you make me a ban - quet for my
4. Your good-ness ___ al - ways is with me and your

1. ev - 'ry thing ___ I need. He lets me rest in the
2. walk there ___ un - a - fraid. E - ven when death is close ___
3. en - e - mies ___ to see. You make me wel-come, ___
4. mer - cy ___ I know. Your lov - ing kind-ness ___

1. mead - ow and leads me to the qui - et streams. He re -
2. ___ I have cour-age, for your help is there. You are
3. pour - ing down hon - or from your might - y hand, and this
4. strength-ens me al - ways as I go through life. I shall

1. stores ___ my soul and he leads me in the paths that are right:
2. close ___ be - side me with com-fort, you are guid - ing my way:
3. joy ___ fills me with glad-ness; it is too much to bear:
4. dwell in your pres-ence for - ev - er, giv-ing praise to your name:

Refrain

Lord, you are my shep-herd, you are my friend.

I want to fol-low you al - ways, just to fol-low my friend.

Text: Based on Psalm 23. Text and music © 1985, Christopher Walker. Published by OCP. All rights reserved.

All Saints/All Souls

Fragrance Prayer

133

Tom Booth

Refrain

Dear Je-sus, help me to spread your fra-grance ev-'ry-where that I go. Dear Je-sus, flood my soul with your spir-it and your love.

1-3 to Verses

Final

Dear Je-sus, dear Je-sus, dear Je-sus.

Verses 1, 2

1. Pen-e-trate and pos-sess my be-ing so ut-ter-ly that all
2. Shine through me and be so in me that ev-'ry soul I come

to Refrain

1. my life may on-ly be a ra-di-ance of you.
2. in con-tact with may feel your pres-ence in my soul.

Verse 3

3. Let them look up and see no long-er me but on-ly you, my Je-sus.

3. Stay with me and then I shall be-gin to shine as you shine so to shine

2 to Refrain

3. as a light to all.

Text: John Henry Newman, 1801–1890; adapt. by Mother Teresa of Calcutta, 1910–1997.
Music © 2000, Tom Booth. Published by spiritandsong.com®, a division of OCP. All rights reserved.

134
In Every Age
Janet Sullivan Whitaker

Verse 1

1. Long be-fore the moun-tains came to be and the land and
1. sea and stars of the night, through the end-less sea-sons of all
1. time, you have al-ways been, you will al-ways be.

Refrain

In ev-'ry age, O God, you have been our ref-uge.

1-3 / to Verses 2, 3 / last time: to Refrain

In ev-'ry age, O God, you have been our hope.

Final

God, you have been our hope, you have been our ref-uge, you have been our hope.

Verse 2

2. Des-ti-ny is cast, and at your si-lent word we re-turn to
2. dust and scat-ter to the wind. A thou-sand years are like a sin-gle mo-ment

to Refrain

2. gone, as the light that fades at the end of day.

Verse 3

3. Teach us to make use of the time we have. Teach us to be
3. pa - tient e - ven as we wait. Teach us to em - brace our ev-'ry joy and
3. pain. To sleep peace - ful - ly, and to rise up strong.

Litany

135

Matt Maher

Cantor   All

1-3. (Saint N.,)   Pray for us. (Saint N.,)

1-3. Pray for us. (Saint N.,)   Pray for us. (Saint N.,)

1, 2

1-3. Pray for us.   (O - ra pro no-bis.) O - ra pro no - bis. 2, 3. (Saint N.,)

Final

3. O - ra pro no-bis. (O - ra pro no -) O - ra pro no - bis.

Prayer of St. Francis/Oración de San Francisco

Sebastian Temple

Verses 1, 2, 4

1. ⁊ Make me a chan-nel of your peace. Where there is ha-tred,
2. ⁊ Make me a chan-nel of your peace. Where there's de-spair in
4. ⁊ Make me a chan-nel of your peace. It is in par-don-

1. *Haz-me un ins-tru-men-to de tu paz,* *don - de ha-ya o - dio*
2. *Haz-me un ins-tru-men-to de tu paz,* *que lle - ve tu es-pe-*
4. *Haz-me un ins-tru-men-to de tu paz,* *es per - do-nan-do*

1. let me bring your love. _____ Where there is in - ju-
2. life, let me bring hope. _____ Where there is dark-ness__
4. ing that we are par-doned, _____ In giv - ing of our-

1. *lle - ve yo tu a - mor, _____* *don - de ha-ya in-ju - ria*
2. *ran - za por do - quier, _____* *don - de ha-ya os-cu - ri -*
4. *que nos das per - dón, _____* *es dan - do a to-dos__*

1. ry, your par-don, Lord, And where there's doubt, true
2. _____ on - ly light, And where there's sad - ness
4. selves that we re - ceive, And in dy - ing that we're

1. *tu per-dón, Se - ñor,* *don - de ha - ya du - da,*
2. *dad lle - ve tu luz,* *don - de ha - ya pe - na,*
4. *____ que tú nos das,* *y mu - rien - do es que vol-*

| 1, Final | 2 |
| 1st time: to Verse 2 (Fine) | to Verse 3 |

1. faith ____ in ____ you.
2. ev - er _____ 2. joy.
4. born to e - ter-nal life.

1. *fe ____ en ____ ti.*
2. *tu go - zo, Se -* *2. ñor.*
4. *ve - mos a na - cer.*

Verse 3

3. O Mas-ter, grant that I may nev-er seek So much to be con-
3. *Ma - es-tro a-yú - da-me a nun-ca bus-car   ser con-so -*

3. soled as to con-sole, _____ To be un-der-stood _ as to un-der-
3. *la - do si - no con - so - lar,   ser en-ten - di - do si - no en-ten-*

to Verse 4

3. stand,   To be loved, as to love, with all my soul.
3. *der,   ser a - ma-do   si - no a - mar.*

Text: Based on the prayer traditionally ascr. to St. Francis of Assisi, ca. 1182–1226.
Text and music © 1967, 2003, OCP. All rights reserved. Dedicated to Mrs. Frances Tracy.

137

Saints of God

Mark Friedman and Janet Vogt

*Any saint, including patron saint of school or parish, may be substituted or added as desired.

All Saints/All Souls

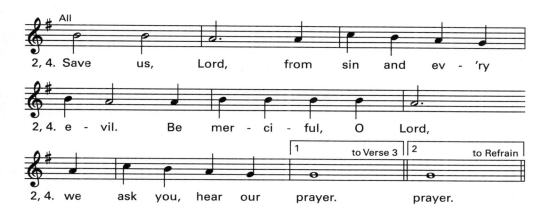

2, 4. Save us, Lord, from sin and ev - 'ry

2, 4. e - vil. Be mer - ci - ful, O Lord,

1 to Verse 3   2 to Refrain

2, 4. we ask you, hear our prayer. prayer.

All Saints/All Souls

Oh, When the Saints

WHEN THE SAINTS

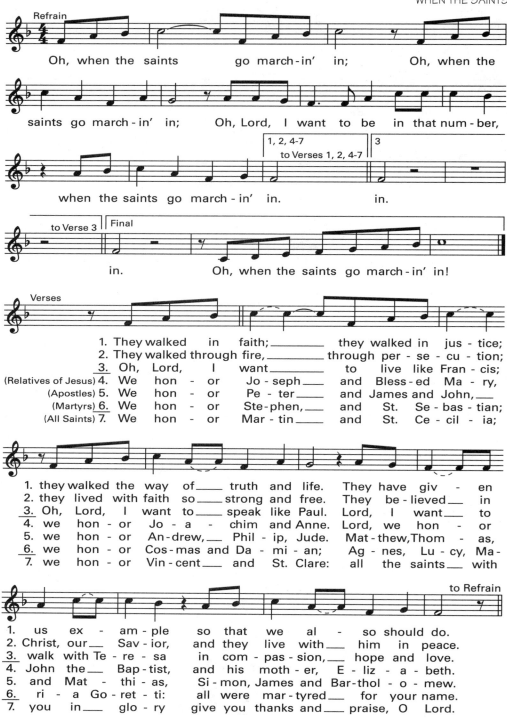

Refrain

Oh, when the saints go march-in' in; Oh, when the
saints go march-in' in; Oh, Lord, I want to be in that num-ber,

1, 2, 4-7
to Verses 1, 2, 4-7

3

when the saints go march-in' in. in.

to Verse 3 | Final

in. Oh, when the saints go march-in' in!

Verses

1. They walked in faith; _____ they walked in jus - tice;
2. They walked through fire, _____ through per - se - cu - tion;
3. Oh, Lord, I want _____ to live like Fran - cis;
(Relatives of Jesus) 4. We hon - or Jo - seph___ and Bless-ed Ma - ry,
(Apostles) 5. We hon - or Pe - ter___ and James and John,___
(Martyrs) 6. We hon - or Ste-phen,___ and St. Se - bas - tian;
(All Saints) 7. We hon - or Mar - tin___ and St. Ce - cil - ia;

1. they walked the way of___ truth and life. They have giv - en
2. they lived with faith so___ strong and free. They be - lieved___ in
3. Oh, Lord, I want to___ speak like Paul. Lord, I want___ to
4. we hon - or Jo - a - chim and Anne. Lord, we hon - or
5. we hon - or An-drew,___ Phil - ip, Jude. Mat - thew, Thom - as,
6. we hon - or Cos-mas and Da - mi - an; Ag - nes, Lu - cy, Ma -
7. we hon - or Vin - cent___ and St. Clare: all the saints___ with

to Refrain

1. us ex - am - ple so that we al - so should do.
2. Christ, our___ Sav - ior, and they live with___ him in peace.
3. walk with Te - re - sa in com - pas - sion,___ hope and love.
4. John the___ Bap - tist, and his moth - er, E - liz - a - beth.
5. and Mat - thi - as, Si - mon, James and Bar - thol - o - mew.
6. ri - a Go - ret - ti: all were mar - tyred___ for your name.
7. you in___ glo - ry give you thanks and___ praise, O Lord.

All Saints/All Souls

For the Beauty of the Earth

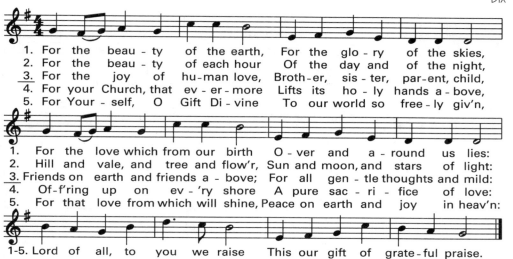

1. For the beau-ty of the earth, For the glo-ry of the skies,
2. For the beau-ty of each hour Of the day and of the night,
3. For the joy of hu-man love, Broth-er, sis-ter, par-ent, child,
4. For your Church, that ev-er-more Lifts its ho-ly hands a-bove,
5. For Your-self, O Gift Di-vine To our world so free-ly giv'n,

1. For the love which from our birth O-ver and a-round us lies:
2. Hill and vale, and tree and flow'r, Sun and moon, and stars of light:
3. Friends on earth and friends a-bove; For all gen-tle thoughts and mild:
4. Of-f'ring up on ev-'ry shore A pure sac-ri-fice of love:
5. For that love from which will shine, Peace on earth and joy in heav'n:

1-5. Lord of all, to you we raise This our gift of grate-ful praise.

Text: 77 77 77; Lyra Eucharistica, 1864; Folliot S. Pierpont, 1835–1917, alt. Music: Conrad Kocher, 1786–1872; adapt. by William H. Monk, 1823–1899.

Thanksgiving

140   Grateful

Tom Tomaszek

Refrain

Grate-ful for the life you give us, thank-ful for your
Grate-ful for the Bread of Heav - en, thank-ful for your

Ho-ly Son, joy - ful in your Spir - it flow - ing
Ho-ly Word, joy - ful in your mer - cy flow - ing,

1 o - ver all, O God of Love.

2 *to Verses* | *Final* we will praise you. we will praise you.

Verses

1. You are more than we i - mag - ine, An-cient, Ho - ly, Liv-
2. May our lives pro-claim your jus - tice, may our voic - es sing

1. - ing Lord. E - ven when we doubt
2. your praise. May our hands work in

1. your pres - ence you are faith - ful to
2. your ser - vice to the glo - ry of

1 *to Refrain* **2** *Interlude* *to Refrain*

1. your Word. 2. your name.

Sacred Creation

(The Canticle of Brother Sun)

141

Rufino Zaragoza, OFM

Refrain

Sa-cred the land, sa-cred the wa-ter, sa-cred the sky, ho-ly and true. Sa-cred all life, sa-cred each oth-er; all re-flect God who is good.

1-3 to Verses

Final
good; all re-flect God, all re-flect God.

Verses

1. All praise be yours through Broth - er Sun,
2. Broth - er Wind and Air that per - vades,
3. Through Broth - er Fire you bright - en the night,

1. bear - ing a like - ness of you, Most High One.
2. var - y their moods to sus - tain all you've made.
3. strong and ro - bust yet play - ful and bright.

1. Sis - ter Moon and Stars who are pre - cious, splen - did,
2. Sis - ter Wa - ter, use - ful and pure, low - ly,
3. Sis - ter Earth, our moth - er who nur - tures, feed - ing,

to Refrain
1. ride your glo - ri - ous sky.
2. free - ly shar - ing her life.
3. yield - ing flow - er and herb.

Text: Based on a text by St. Francis of Assisi, ca. 1182–1226, and the inspiration of Louis Vitale, OFM; Rufino Zaragoza, OFM.
Text and music © 1990, Rufino Zaragoza, OFM. Published by OCP. All rights reserved.

Thanksgiving

142 Thank You, God

Janet Vogt

Verses

1. Thank you, God, for sim-ple gifts, songs to sing and
2. Thank you, God, for fam-i-ly. Thank you, God, for
3. Thank you for the bread of life, thank you for the
4. Thank you for the heav'n-ly place we can go to

1. morn-ing skies, hands to hold and stars at night,
2. spe-cial friends, for peace and joy that nev-er ends,
3. bless-ing cup giv-en by your pre-cious love,
4. seek your grace, there our hearts and trea-sures lay,

1, 3 *to Verses 2, 4* **2, 4**

1-4. we want to thank you, God. 2, 4.

Refrain

Thank you, God. Thank you, God. With our love we come to thank you,

God. Thank you ev-'ry day and in ev-'ry way; we want to thank

1 *to Verse 3* **3** **Final**

you, God. We want to thank you, God.

We want to thank you, *God.

*Alternate melody note.

With All Our Hearts

143

Jesse Manibusan

Refrain

We praise you, God of life, sa - cred and good.

We thank you, God of hope, faith - ful and true.

We praise you, God of love, in all we are.

We thank you, God, with all our hearts.

Verses

1. In our fear we lose our sens - es, for - get - ting
2. When our ig - no - rance con - fines us, we are con -
3. When the light of hope is fad - ing, when judg - ment

1. all we are. But your love is un - re - lent - ing,
2. sumed by fear. Your a - maz - ing grace un - binds us,
3. tears us down, help us see in ev - 'ry per - son

to Refrain

1. heal - ing ev - 'ry bro - ken heart.
2. giv - ing us the strength to care.
3. ho - li - ness where you are found.

Thanksgiving

144   Come to Us

Steve Angrisano

Refrain

Melody: Come to us, Je - sus, come to us. Come to us,

Harmony: We are wait - ing, hope-ful, an - tic - i - pat-ing. We are

1. Je - sus. 2. Je - sus, come. *(to Verses)* come. *(Final)* come.

wait - ing. Je - sus, come. come. come.

Verse 1

1. For a world filled with dark - ness longs to see your light.

1. For a world of de-spair a-waits that hope - ful night. *(to Refrain)*

Verse 2

2. We know not where this jour - ney leads, we fol-low just our dreams.

2. We trav-el far that we might kneel be-fore a new-born King. *(to Refrain)*

Verse 3

3. Un-to us a shin - ing star, a sign for all to see:

3. that un-to us a child is born, born to set us free. *(to Refrain)*

Advent

O Come, Emmanuel

145

Mark Friedman and Janet Vogt

Refrain

O come, Em-man-u-el, and in-to our hearts be born. Make read-y his path with joy-ful praise, pre-par-ing the way of the Lord. O come, O Prince of Peace, for proph-ets did long fore-tell the one who will reign for-ev-er-more, O come, Em-man-u-el.

1-4 / **2 to Verses**

Final

el. O come, Em-man-u-el.

Verses — **Cantor**

1. A her-ald's voice is heard:
2. The son of Da-vid comes
3. Pro-claim from moun-tains high
4. Come now with jus-tice, Lord,

All — **Cantor**

1. "Make straight his way." All peo-ple will
2. for all to save, to come and shine
3. the Lord has come, the Word now made
4. and set us free. Be crowned with the

to Refrain

1. know of God's glo-ry in ev-'ry age.
2. forth with the dawn-ing of end-less day.
3. flesh in our Sav-ior, the Ho-ly One.
4. glo-ry of won-der and maj-es-ty.

Advent

146

Come, Lord Jesus

Steve Angrisano and Tom Tomaszek

Refrain
Come, Lord Je - sus, come. Come and fill my heart with your life. Hold me close, Lord, hold me tight, and come, Lord Je - sus, come.

repeat 1st time to Verses/Interlude

Last time
Hold me close, Lord, hold me tight.

Come, Lord Je - sus, come.

Verse 1
1. Where there's de - spair in life, Lord, let me be your voice of hope. Where there's in - ju - ry, Lord, *to Refrain* let me be your voice of peace.

Verse 2
2. Where there is sad - ness let me be your com - fort and your joy. When there's fear in our hearts *to Refrain* let me be a sign of faith.

Text: Verses based on a prayer ascribed to St. Francis of Assisi, ca. 1182–1226.
Text and music © 1997, Steve Angrisano and Thomas N. Tomaszek. Published by spiritandsong.com®, a division of OCP. All rights reserved.

Advent

Ready the Way

Curtis Stephan

Refrain

Read-y the way, read-y the way, read-y the way

1. of the Lord.
2. of the Lord.

Verse 1

1. Make straight the road, raise the val - leys, and
1. moun-tains make low. Turn-ing from sin, let the bro-ken be whole,

to Refrain

1. and read - y the way of the Lord.

Verses 2, 3

2. As we wait for you, give us the strength to walk
3. Let us see your face; in our hearts we pre-

2. in your truth, so we may love more like you
3. - pare a place. Come bring this world your mer - cy and grace

to Refrain

2. and
3. as we } read - y the way for you, Lord.

Text: Based on Isaiah 40:3, 4a. Text and music © 2004, Curtis Stephan. Published by spiritandsong.com®, a division of OCP. All rights reserved.

*Last time: Repeat final phrase.

Advent

148 Emmanuel

Steve Angrisano

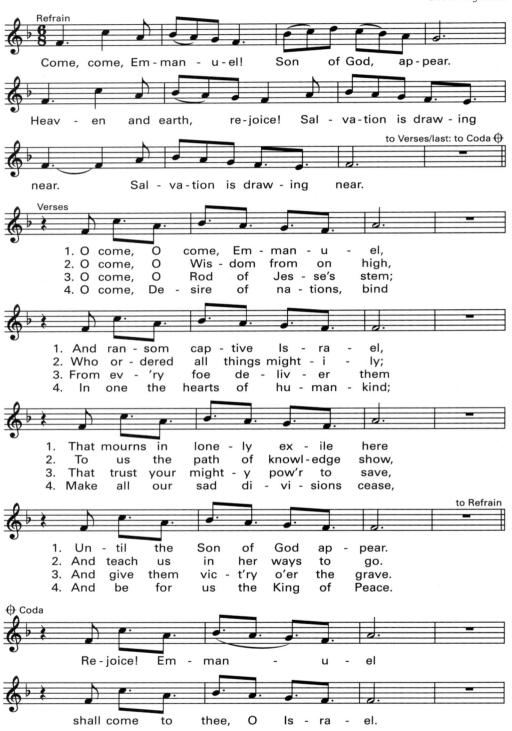

Refrain

Come, come, Em-man-u-el! Son of God, ap-pear.

Heav-en and earth, re-joice! Sal-va-tion is draw-ing

to Verses/last: to Coda

near. Sal-va-tion is draw-ing near.

Verses

1. O come, O come, Em-man-u-el,
2. O come, O Wis-dom from on high,
3. O come, O Rod of Jes-se's stem;
4. O come, De-sire of na-tions, bind

1. And ran-som cap-tive Is-ra-el,
2. Who or-dered all things might-i-ly;
3. From ev-'ry foe de-liv-er them
4. In one the hearts of hu-man-kind;

1. That mourns in lone-ly ex-ile here
2. To us the path of knowl-edge show,
3. That trust your might-y pow'r to save,
4. Make all our sad di-vi-sions cease,

to Refrain

1. Un-til the Son of God ap-pear.
2. And teach us in her ways to go.
3. And give them vic-t'ry o'er the grave.
4. And be for us the King of Peace.

Coda

Re-joice! Em-man-u-el

shall come to thee, O Is-ra-el.

Advent

Re - joice! Em - man - u - el shall come to thee, O Is - ra - el.

Encircle This Wreath

149

Mark Friedman and Janet Vogt

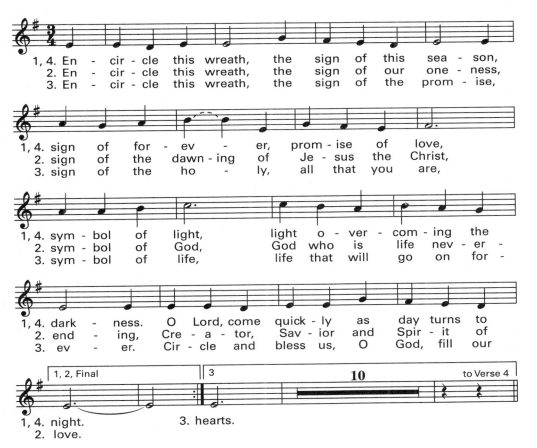

1, 4. En - cir - cle this wreath, the sign of this sea - son,
2. En - cir - cle this wreath, the sign of our one - ness,
3. En - cir - cle this wreath, the sign of the prom - ise,

1, 4. sign of for - ev - er, prom - ise of love,
2. sign of the dawn - ing of Je - sus the Christ,
3. sign of the ho - ly, all that you are,

1, 4. sym - bol of light, light o - ver - com - ing the
2. sym - bol of God, God who is life nev - er -
3. sym - bol of life, life that will go on for -

1, 4. dark - ness. O Lord, come quick - ly as day turns to
2. end - ing, Cre - a - tor, Sav - ior and Spir - it of
3. ev - er. Cir - cle and bless us, O God, fill our

1, 2, Final | *3* | **10** | *to Verse 4*

1, 4. night.
3. hearts.
2. love.

150   Find Us Ready

Tom Booth

Refrain

Find us read-y, Lord, not stand-ing still.
Find us work-ing and lov-ing and do-ing
your will. Find us read-y, Lord, faith-ful in
love, build-ing the king-dom that's
here and a-bove, build-ing the
king-dom of mer-cy and love.

Verses

1. We must wait for the Lord   for we
2. We must make straight the path,   God's
3. Lift-ing up those bowed down,   we pre-

1. know not the time.   So here and to-day
2. love re-vealed.   With sin cast a-side,
3. pare for our God.   Re-joice in the Lord,

1. we gath-er and pray,   dis-
2. God's mer-cy a-live,
3. for hope has been born   in

to Refrain

1. cov-er-ing love in our midst.
2. fear not for here is your God.
3. hearts where our God finds a home.

Advent

Optional Final Ending: (Repeat as needed)

Brick by brick, stone by stone, find us work-ing and lov-ing and do-ing your will. Find us read-y, Lord, faith-ful in love. build-ing the king-dom that's here and a-bove.

O Come, O Come, Emmanuel   151

VENI, VENI, EMMANUEL

1. O come, O come, Emmanuel,
   And ransom captive Israel,
   That mourns in lonely exile here
   Until the Son of God appear.

Refrain
   Rejoice! Rejoice! Emmanuel
   Shall come to thee, O Israel!

2. O come, Thou Wisdom from on high,
   Who ord'rest all things mightily;
   To us the path of knowledge show,
   And teach us in her ways to go.

3. O come, O come, Thou Lord of might,
   Who to thy tribes on Sinai's height
   In ancient times didst give the law,
   In cloud and majesty and awe.

4. O come, Thou Rod of Jesse's stem,
   From ev'ry foe deliver them
   That trust thy mighty pow'r to save,
   And give them vict'ry o'er the grave.

5. O come, Thou Key of David, come,
   And open wide our heav'nly home;
   Make safe the way that leads on high,
   And close the path to misery.

6. O come, Thou Dayspring from on high
   And cheer us by thy drawing nigh;
   Disperse the gloomy clouds of night,
   And death's dark shadow put to flight.

7. O come, Desire of nations, bind
   In one the hearts of all humankind;
   Bid thou our sad divisions cease,
   And be thyself our Prince of Peace.

Text: LM with refrain; Latin, 9th cent.; tr. by John M. Neale, 1818–1866, alt.
Music: Chant, Mode I; adapt. by Thomas Helmore, 1811–1890.

152

We Shall Prepare

Janet Vogt

Refrain

We shall pre-pare our hearts for new love. We shall pre-pare our
eyes for the blind-ing light. We shall pre-pare our faith to break the
dark of night. We shall pre-pare the way of the Lord! *(1-3 to Verses)*

Final

Lord. We shall pre-pare the way of the Lord!

Verses

1. A voice strong and clear cries out in the night:
2. There shall be one___ who is to come,
3. Chil-dren of God,___ come change your hearts.

1. "Make straight the way of our God."
2. might-i-er than you or I.
3. Come to the wa-ter of life.

1. The moun-tains bend low,___ the plains will rise up
2. We shall be changed,___ bap-tized with fire
3. Of-fer your hand,___ of-fer your heart

to Refrain

1. to the glo-ry, the glo-ry of God!
2. of the spir-it, the spir-it of God!
3. to the peo-ple, the peo-ple of God!

Advent

Waiting in Silence

Carey Landry

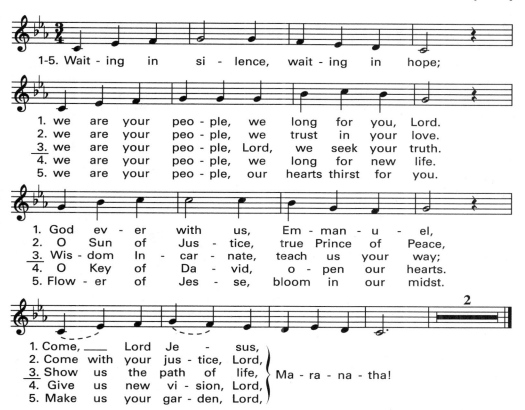

1-5. Wait - ing in si - lence, wait - ing in hope;

1. we are your peo - ple, we long for you, Lord.
2. we are your peo - ple, we trust in your love.
3. we are your peo - ple, Lord, we seek your truth.
4. we are your peo - ple, we long for new life.
5. we are your peo - ple, our hearts thirst for you.

1. God ev - er with us, Em - man - u - el,
2. O Sun of Jus - tice, true Prince of Peace,
3. Wis - dom In - car - nate, teach us your way;
4. O Key of Da - vid, o - pen our hearts.
5. Flow - er of Jes - se, bloom in our midst.

1. Come, ___ Lord Je - sus,
2. Come with your jus - tice, Lord,
3. Show us the path of life, } Ma - ra - na - tha!
4. Give us new vi - sion, Lord,
5. Make us your gar - den, Lord,

Advent

154

By the Star

Janet Vogt

Refrain

By the star in the night I will fol-low my Lord.

I will seek and I know I will find, for the star shin-ing bright

lights the way through the night. Gen-tle star shin-ing

bright, lead me home by the love of God's light.

Verses

1. God, in his mer-cy and in-fi-nite love, sent forth a light in the
2. Shep-herds a-bid-ing their flocks by __ night looked to the heav-en-ly
3. O star of Beth-le-hem, O star of night, bless-ed and won-der-ful

1. night. Shin-ing from hea-ven to bid all to come to
2. light. An-gels cried out that a child has been born, a
3. sight; shin-ing so bright-ly for all to __ see the

to Refrain

1. wor-ship the ba-by, Ma-ry's lit-tle son.
2. child known as Je-sus, who is Christ the Lord.
3. love of our Lord for e-ter-ni-ty.

Christmas

Love Has Come

155

Matt Maher

Verses

1. With one voice the an - gels sing
2. God the Fa - ther, El - o - him,
3. God of Cov - e - nant, di - vine,
4. Now sal - va - tion has ___ come

1. songs that make cre - a - tion ring.
2. voice of thun - der, spir - it, wind:
3. lead us to the end of time,
4. in the New Je - ru - sa - lem.

1. Proph - ets hear and call us to
2. breathe on me your ver - y life;
3. be - yond sor - row, be - yond fear,
4. Danc - ers dance and sing - ers roar; pro -

1. live in spir - it and in truth. (to Verse 2)
2. grace will make the dark - ness bright.
3. be - yond pride and earth - en tears.
4. claim - ing Je - sus Christ is Lord!

Refrain

Word of God, en - throned, dwell in us for - ev - er -

more. Love has come to show the way.

Hal - le - lu - jah, peace be with

us. Love has come to show the way.

156 Love So Bright

Gerard Chiusano

1. O ti - ny babe, sleep be - side your moth-er on this

1. night. You are born to all the world to shine your ho - ly light.

1. Do we know the strength you have, e - ven though so small?

1. Your ti - ny hands will hold the world and bring peace to all.

Refrain

O ho - ly child, keep us near your flame to-night, and

lift this wea - ry world with your love so bright. Your

joy sur-rounds us now, we feel your ten - der

might: keep us safe and close to you with your

1-3 love so bright. *3 to Verses* *Final* bright.

Verse 2

2. On this night, an - gels sing in joy - ous praise to

Christmas

2. you: "You were born to be our king and make our hearts a-new!"

2. Your love has come to us, you've o-pened ev - 'ry door, and

to Refrain

2. with your birth the dark - ness is gone for ev - er - more!

Verse 3

3. Close to Ma - ry now is the beat-ing of your

3. heart, a heart we know that holds our love and can't be torn a-part.

3. Close your eyes in slum - ber, you, our new-born king,

to Refrain

3. brought to us to save our souls that will for-ev - er sing:

Verse 4

4. With your com - ing to us, we shall now be strong. The world has

4. wait - ed for this peace, wait-ed for so long. So, with all the

4. an - gels we re-joice and sing your praise. We

to Refrain

4. know that you will guide us; you will light all our days!

157 Praise Him with Cymbals

Janet Vogt

Verses

1. In a low - ly man-ger on a dark win-ter's night, a
2. Three _ wise _ men came to him, _ bear - ing gifts of
3. All _ heav-en shall praise him and _ lift up their voice to

1. star _ a - rose in the sky, and _ to the
2. frank - in - cense, myrrh _ and gold; for the King of
3. sing of his won - der - ful birth: for the Son of

1. Earth it gave a great light, a bright and glo - ri - ous sign.
2. kings was born on that night, as they so wise - ly fore - told.
3. man was born on that night, and brought God's love to the Earth.

Refrain

O praise him with cym - bals, praise him with danc - ing,

praise him with glad tam - bou - rines. And praise him with

sing - ing, praise him with clap - ping, Je - sus is born, Christ the

1, 2 to Verses 2, 3

King. | Final King.

Je - sus is born, Christ the King!

Go, Tell It on the Mountain

Refrain

Go, tell it on the moun-tain, o-ver the hills and ev-'ry-where;

go, tell it on the moun - tain that Je - sus Christ is born. *(1-4, to Verses)*

Je - sus Christ is born. *(5, to Refrain)* Je - sus Christ is born. *(Final)*

Verses

1. While shep-herds kept their watch-ing o'er si - lent flocks by night,
2. The shep-herds feared and trem-bled when high a - bove the earth
3. And lo, when they had heard it, they all bowed down and prayed;
4. Down in a low - ly man - ger the hum - ble Christ was born,

1. be - hold, through-out the heav-ens there shone a ho - ly light.
2. rang out the an - gel cho - rus that hailed our Sav - ior's birth.
3. they trav - eled on to - geth - er to where the Babe was laid.
4. and God sent us sal - va - tion that bless - ed Christ-mas morn.

(to Refrain)

Text: 76 76 with refrain; John W. Work, Jr., 1872–1925, alt.; from *American Negro Songs and Spirituals*, 1940, © Mrs. John W. Work III.
Music: African American Spiritual.

Hark! The Herald Angels Sing

1. Hark! the herald angels sing:
"Glory to the newborn King;
Peace on earth, and mercy mild,
God and sinners reconciled!"
Joyful, all ye nations, rise,
Join the triumph of the skies;
With angelic hosts proclaim:
"Christ is born in Bethlehem!"

Refrain
Hark! the herald angels sing,
"Glory to the newborn King."

2. Christ, by highest heav'n adored,
Christ, the everlasting Lord;

Late in time, behold him come,
Offspring of a virgin's womb.
Veiled in flesh the Godhead see!
Hail th'incarnate Deity!
Pleased as man with us to dwell;
Jesus, our Emmanuel!

3. Hail the heav'n-born Prince of Peace!
Hail the Sun of Righteousness!
Light and life to all he brings,
Ris'n with healing in his wings.
Mild he lays his glory by,
Born that we no more may die,
Born to raise us from the earth,
Born to give us second birth.

Text: 77 77 D with refrain; Charles Wesley, 1707–1788, alt.
Music: Felix Mendelssohn, 1809–1847; adapt. by William H. Cummings, 1831–1915.

Christmas

160 God So Loved the World

Gerard Chiusano

1. A man-ger his throne, a sta-ble his court; the
2. Hu-man like us in all things but sin; the
3. Let us re-joice, let us be glad;

1. King of cre-a-tion in hum-ble at-tire. No
2. King of cre-a-tion knew hun-ger and pain.
3. Come, let us sing of sal-va-tion in Christ.

1. fan-fare, no trum-pet, yet an-gels sing on high:
2. Born in-to weak-ness, yet Son of God Most High:
3. All of the na-tions have seen the pow'r of God:

1. "Pro-claim the good news, the Sav-ior is born!"
2. Sing our sal-va-tion, the Sav-ior is born!
3. Sing out a new song, the Sav-ior is born!

Refrain

For God so loved the world, he gave his on-ly Son,

that all who be-lieve in him might live. We praise his

ho-ly birth, God's love re-vealed to earth; God's

1, 2
1: to Verse 2
2: to Interlude

heart of com-pas-sion, giv-en in Christ our Lord.

Final

Lord. Al - le - lu - ia, al - le - lu - ia.

Al - le-lu-ia, al - le-lu - ia.

Interlude

Al - le-lu - ia, al - le-lu - ia. Praise to Al -

migh-ty God on high. Al - le - lu - ia, al - le - lu - ia.

to Verse 3

Al - le - lu-ia, al - le-lu - ia.

Text: Refrain based on John 3:16. Text and music © 1997, Gerard Chiusano. Published by OCP. All rights reserved.

Joy to the World

161

ANTIOCH

1. Joy to the world! the Lord is come;
   Let earth receive her King;
   Let every heart prepare him room,
   And heaven and nature sing,
   And heaven and nature sing,
   And heaven, and heaven and nature sing.

2. Joy to the world! the Savior reigns;
   Let us our songs employ;
   While fields and floods,
        rocks, hills and plains

Repeat the sounding joy,
Repeat the sounding joy,
Repeat, repeat the sounding joy.

3. He rules the world with truth and grace,
   And makes the nations prove
   The glories of his righteousness,
   And wonders of his love,
   And wonders of his love,
   And wonders, wonders of his love.

Text: CM with repeats; based on Psalm 98:4–9; Isaac Watts, 1674–1748, alt. Music: T. Hawkes' Collection of Tunes, 1833; George Frideric Handel, 1685–1759.

162   O Come, All Ye Faithful/Adeste Fideles

ADESTE FIDELES

1. O Come, all ye faithful,
    joyful and triumphant,
   O come ye, O come ye to Bethlehem;
   Come and behold him,
    born the King of angels;
   O come, let us adore him,
   O come, let us adore him,
   O come, let us adore him, Christ, the Lord!

2. Sing, choirs of angels, sing in exultation,
   Sing, all ye citizens of heav'n above!
   Glory to God, all glory in the highest;
   O come, let us adore him,
   O come, let us adore him,
   O come, let us adore him, Christ, the Lord!

3. Yea, Lord, we greet thee, born this
    happy morning,
   Jesus, to thee be all glory giv'n;
   Word of the Father, now in flesh
    appearing;
   O come, let us adore him,
   O come, let us adore him,
   O come, let us adore him, Christ, the Lord!

4. Adéste fidéles, laeti triumphántes,
   Veníte, veníte in Béthlehem.
   Natum vidéte, Regem angelórum.
   Veníte, adorémus, veníte, adorémus,
   veníte, adorémus Dóminum.

Text: Irregular with refrain; John F. Wade, ca. 1711–1786; tr. by Frederick Oakeley, 1802–1880, alt. Music: John F. Wade.

163   Silent Night, Holy Night

STILLE NACHT

1. Silent night! Holy night!
   All is calm, all is bright
   Round yon Virgin Mother and child!
   Holy Infant so tender and mild,
   Sleep in heavenly peace,
   Sleep in heavenly peace.

2. Silent night! Holy night!
   Shepherds quake at the sight;
   Glories stream from heaven afar;

   Heav'nly hosts sing "Alleluia!
   Christ the Savior is born,
   Christ the Savior is born."

3. Silent night! Holy night!
   Son of God, love's pure light
   Radiant beams from thy holy face,
   With the dawn of redeeming grace,
   Jesus, Lord, at thy birth,
   Jesus, Lord, at thy birth.

Text: 66 89 66; Joseph Mohr, 1792–1849; tr. by John F. Young, 1820–1885. Music: Franz X. Grüber, 1787–1863.

1. We three kings of Orient are;
   Bearing gifts we traverse afar,
   Field and fountain, Moor and mountain,
   Following yonder star.

Refrain
   O star of wonder, star of night,
   Star with royal beauty bright;
   Westward leading, still proceeding,
   Guide us to thy perfect light.

2. Born a King on Bethlehem's plain,
   Gold I bring to crown him again,
   King forever, Ceasing never
   Over us all to reign.

3. Frankincense to offer have I:
   Incense owns a Deity nigh;
   Prayer and praising, Gladly raising,
   Worship him, God on high.

4. Myrrh is mine; its bitter perfume
   Breathes a life of gathering gloom;
   Sorrowing, sighing, Bleeding, dying,
   Sealed in the stone-cold tomb.

5. Glorious now, behold him arise,
   King and God and Sacrifice;
   "Alleluia, alleluia!"
   Sounds through the earth and skies.

Text: 88 44 6 with refrain; based on Matthew 2:1–11. Text and music: John H. Hopkins Jr., 1820–1891, alt.

What Child Is This

165

GREENSLEEVES

1. What child is this, who laid to rest,
   On Mary's lap is sleeping?
   Whom angels greet with anthems sweet,
   While shepherds watch are keeping?

Refrain
   This, this is Christ the King,
   Whom shepherds guard and angels sing;
   Haste, haste to bring him laud,
   the babe, the son of Mary.

2. Why lies he in such mean estate
   Where ox and ass are feeding?
   Good Christian, fear: for sinners here
   The silent Word is pleading.

3. So bring him incense, gold, and myrrh,
   Come peasant, king, to own him;
   The Kings of kings salvation brings,
   Let loving hearts enthrone him.

Text: 87 87 with refrain; William C. Dix, 1837–1898. Music: Trad. English Melody, 16th cent.

Cry the Gospel

Tom Booth

Verses 1, 2

1. You are the light of the world, you are the light
2. You are the salt of the earth, you are the salt

1. of the world. Shine for all ___ to see, so in the
2. of the earth, bring-ing mer-cy and peace to ev-'ry

1. Fa-ther they'll be-lieve. You are the light of the world.
2. per-son that you meet. You are the salt of the earth.

Refrain
Cantor

(Say not that you are

All

too young.) "We are ho - ly we are strong!"

All

(With pur-i-ty and love and faith,) "Pro -

claim-ing Christ to-day!" be ho - ly. The

Lord be glor-i-fied! Be ho - ly, cry the gos -

- pel with your life! Stand-ing at the gate-way of our faith,

on the rock of Pe-ter and the saints, with the

Ho-ly Spir-it show-ing us the way to be

ho - ly, and cry the gos - pel, cry the gos-

- pel with your life!

Verse 3

3. Lord, we come to do your will. Yes, Lord, we

3. come to do your will. Not on - ly in our words, but in our

to Refrain

3. liv - ing it is heard: Lord, we come to do your will.

167 We Are God's Work of Art

Mark Friedman

Refrain: 1st time: Cantor, All repeat; thereafter: All

We are God's work of art. And in Christ we are
So-mos o-bra de Dios, en Cris-to for-

fash-ioned in __ love. With God's grace in our heart
ma-dos en a-mor. Con Dios en nues-tro co-ra-zón

__ we will rise up in glo-ry with Christ, in glo-ry with
glo-ri-fi-ca-mos a Cris - to, a Cris-to

1, Final / **2-4** to Verses / **5**

Christ, our light! light! light! We are God's work of
nues-tra luz. luz. luz. So-mos o-bra de

Verses

1. We were dead in sin but God's
2. All cre-a-tion sings of the
3. You have cho-sen us as your

1. glo-ry en-tered in, bring-ing us hope,
2. beau-ty of all things formed by our God,
3. chil-dren, one in love. Close to your heart,

1. fill-ing us with new life! ⎫ We are God's work of
2. fill-ing us with new hope! ⎬ *So-mos o-bra de*
3. we are your work of art! ⎭

They'll Know We Are Christians

168

ST. BRENDAN'S

Verses

1. We are one in the Spir-it, we are one in the Lord,
2. We will walk with each oth-er, we will walk hand in hand,
3. We will work with each oth-er, we will work side by side,
4. All ___ praise to the Fa-ther, from ___ whom all things come,

1. We are one in the Spir-it, we are one in the Lord,
2. We will walk with each oth-er, we will walk hand in hand,
3. We will work with each oth-er, we will work side by side,
4. And all praise to Christ Je-sus, his ___ on - ly ___ Son,

1. And we pray that all u - ni - ty may one day be re - stored.
2. And to - geth - er we'll spread the news that God is in our land.
3. And we'll guard each one's dig - ni - ty and save ___ each one's pride.
4. And all praise to the Spir - it, who ___ makes ___ us ___ one.

Refrain

And they'll know we are Chris-tians by our love, by our

love, Yes they'll know we are Chris-tians by our love.

Text: 13 13 14 with refrain; Peter Scholtes. Music: Peter Scholtes. Text and music © 1966, F.E.L. Publications, Ltd., assigned 1991 to the Lorenz Corp. All rights reserved. International copyright secured. Used with permission.

Catholic Schools Week

169

We Shall Be the Light

Janet Vogt and Mark Friedman

Verses

Cantor ... *All*

1. Stand-ing by a friend in need,_____
2. Un - der bush - els, nev - er hid - den,
3. Out of dark - ness we shall come;_____

} we shall be the light,

1-3. we shall be the light, be the light of God.

Cantor ... *All*

1. In our words and in our deeds,_____
2. Saved by grace, in love for - giv - en,
3. Like a can - dle in the night,_____

} we shall be the light,

1-3. we shall be the light of God.

Refrain

All ... Cantor

We shall be the light of God, a light for all the world

All ... Cantor

to see; be the light of God, a cit - y on a hill.

All

Though the path is dark, your word's a lamp un-to our feet

1, 2 — 1st time: to Verse 2

2

for all who seek to be the light of God.

*Cue notes are an alternative (higher) melody.

God's light is burn - ing, God's light is burn - ing in us.

to Verse 3

God's light is burn - ing, God's light is burn - ing in us.

3   to Refrain | Final

be the light of God. We shall be the light of God's light

is burn - ing, God's light is burn - ing in us.

God's light is burn - ing, God's light is burn - ing in us.

God's light is burn - ing, God's light is burn - ing in us.

God's light is burn - ing. Be the light of God!

170 Ashes

Tom Conry

1. We rise a-gain from ash-es, from the good we've failed to
2. We of-fer you our fail-ures, we ___ of-fer you at-
3. Then rise a-gain from ash-es, let ___ heal-ing come to
4. ₹ Thanks be to the Fa-ther, who ___ made us like him-

1. do. We rise a-gain from ash-es, to cre-ate our-selves a-
2. tempts, the gifts not ful-ly giv-en, the ___ dreams not ful-ly
3. pain, though spring has turned to win-ter, and ___ sun-shine turned to
4. self. ₹ Thanks be to his Son, ___ who ___ saved us by his

1. new. If ___ all our world is ash-es, then ___ must our lives be
2. dreamt. Give our stum-bl-ings di-rec-tion, give our vi-sions wid-er
3. rain. The ___ rain we'll use for grow-ing, and cre-ate the world a-
4. death. ₹ Thanks be to the Spir-it who cre-ates the world a-

1. true, an ___ of-fer-ing of ash-es, an of-fer-ing to you.
2. view, an ___ of-fer-ing of ash-es, an of-fer-ing to you.
3. new from an of-fer-ing of ash-es, an of-fer-ing to you.
4. new from an of-fer-ing of ash-es, an of-fer-ing to you.

171 Sign Us with Ashes

Mark Friedman and Janet Vogt

Refrain

Sign us with ash-es, the sign of your cross. Give us the

grace to know your mer-cy, Lord. Re-new our spir-its and

1st time: Repeat

o-pen our hearts. Help us re-mem-ber the love you gave us.

Ash Wednesday

With These Ashes

172

Gerard Chiusano

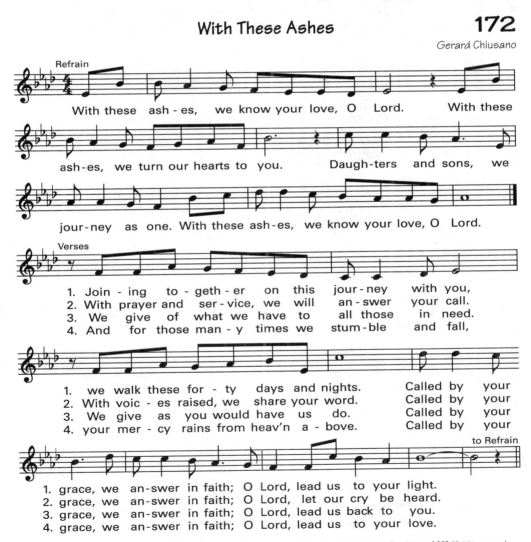

Ash Wednesday

40 Days

Matt Maher

1. For-ty days to ___ wan - der, for-ty days to die
2. For-ty days to re - mem - ber the ___ Pas - chal Sac-

1. to self. For-ty days to grow strong - er as faith
2. - ri-fice. For-ty days to dis - cov - er his pas-

1. breaks o - pen the gates of hell. The ju - bi-lee is
2. - sion calls us ___ to new life. The ju - bi-lee is

1. o - ver, but grace is far from gone in the hearts of the
2. o - ver, but mer - cy's far from gone in the arms of the

1. faith - ful, bro-ken on the wheels of love.
2. fa - ther as the way - ward child comes home.

Refrain

'Cause in the des - ert of temp - ta - tion lies the

storm of true con - ver - sion, where springs of liv - ing wa -

- ter drown and re-fresh you. And as the

Jor-dan pours out change, your true self is all that re-mains,

where springs of liv - ing wa - ter bind and break

you, bind and break you.

you, bind and break you, bind and break

you, bind and break you.

Let the Wind Blow

174

Janet Vogt

Refrain: 1st time: Cantor; thereafter: All

Let the wind blow, let the wa-ters know. Tell the earth, the

stars, the sun: bless-ed Je - sus, born to save us all; the ap-

Verses

point - ed hour has come.
1. I have heard the peo - ple cry out
2. I have heard the roost - er crow three
3. I have seen the sun - light dis - ap-

1. loud: "Cru - ci - fy him, cru - ci - fy him now! If you are the
2. times. I have seen the sor - row in their eyes as the peo - ple
3. pear. I have seen the heav - ens rain with tears as the dark-ness

to Refrain

1. one you say you are, where is your God?"
2. fled in fear and turned their backs on God.
3. robbed the day and took our hope a - way.

Lent & Holy Week

175   Healing Hands

Joshua Blakesley

Verses

1. I've fall-en, Lord, ∿ pick me up, ∿ hold me close.
2. Com-fort me, Lord, show me your love, ∿ fill my soul.
3. Speak to me, Lord, ∿ say the words I need to hear
4. Strength-en me, Lord, ∿ I am weak, but you are strong.

1. I___ need for-give - ness a-gain. I've come so
2. I___ don't see clear-ly an-y-more. I try so
3. when it seems so hard___ to un-der-stand. I get so
4. Christ,___ lead me through___ an-oth-er day. I need your

1. far down this road that you have shown___ me,
2. hard to___ see your face in all___ I do.
3. lost with the thoughts___ in my head,_____
4. help; please___ come and res - cue me._____

1. but some-times___ I just_____ don't see___ the end.
2. ∿ I just___ for - get___ what I'm look - ing for.
3. ∿ I can't___ re - mem - ber who___ I am.
4. ∿ Guide___ me and show___ me your way.

1	to Verse 2	2-4
	4	

1.   2-4.

Refrain

Your heal - ing hands will al - ways em-brace me. Your heal-ing hands won't let me go. Your heal - ing hands pour your love up-on me, fill-ing my heart, mak-ing me whole.

1	to Verse 3	2 to Verse 4	Final
	4		

Make me whole.

Lent & Holy Week

From a King to a King

Janet Vogt

Refrain

From a king to a king of kings, from a crown of gold

to a crown of thorns, from a king so loved to a

king so scorned, God weaves our lives. From the

fields of a shep-herd boy to the shep-herd who we

now a-dore, from a might-y king to a gen-tle Lord, God

to Verse 1 — *2, 3* — *to Verses 2, 3*

weaves our lives. weaves our lives.

Final

weaves our lives. God weaves our lives.

Verses

1. O Da-vid, cho-sen one,__ you slay the might-y foe.
2. O Da-vid, sing your songs__ of faith for-ev-er-more.
3. O Lord, I shall not want____ for you lead-eth me

to Refrain

1. And all will call you blessed as life from life un-folds.
2. With sounds of sweet re-frains, pre-pare the way of the Lord.
3. be-side still wa-ters and to lie in pas-tures green.

177

Above All

Lenny LeBlanc and Paul Baloche

and thought of me a-bove all.

In the Silence of the Garden

178

Janet Vogt

Refrain: 1st time: Cantor, All repeat; thereafter: All

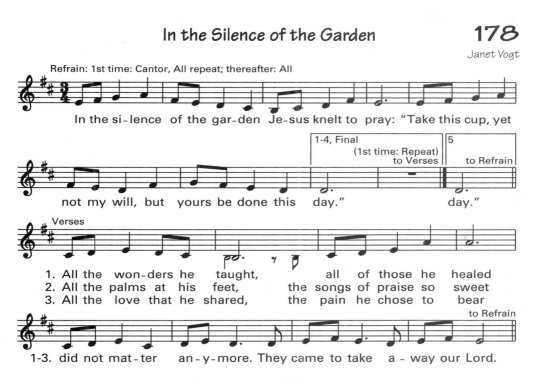

In the si-lence of the gar-den Je-sus knelt to pray: "Take this cup, yet

not my will, but yours be done this day." day."

Verses

1. All the won-ders he taught, all of those he healed
2. All the palms at his feet, the songs of praise so sweet
3. All the love that he shared, the pain he chose to bear

1-3. did not mat-ter an-y-more. They came to take a-way our Lord.

179

I Thirst

Cyprian Consiglio

Ostinato Refrain: 1st time: Cantor, 2nd time: All; All sing once between verses

I thirst! I ache! I hun-ger!

to Verses 3, 4

I need you!

Verse 1

1. When the times are good and the days run long and I love my-self a-

1. gain, I re-joice to know that it's been your love that has

to Refrain

1. pulled me through a-gain. I need you!

Verse 2

2. When I hold the hand of my friend or my neigh-bor and I'm

2. one with all who live, and at the end of an-oth-er long hard day when I've

2. giv-en all I can give, I need you!

Ostinato Refrain

I thirst! I ache! I hun-ger! I

1.
4 repeat Refrain 2, 3
to Verses 3, 4

need you! you!

Verse 3

3. When I hate my neigh-bor and don't pray for my foes and it

3. does-n't feel that wrong, when the on-ly rea-son that I keep on sing-ing is

to Refrain

3. just for the sake of the song, I need you!

Verse 4 (twice)

4. Come then, Lord, come, Sav - ior, Might-y One, fill my life with
   (you. Come, Lord,)

4. sweet - ness. Swift - ly Lord, now the skies are an - gry, I

4. need to know your peace. I need you!

Text: Based on Psalm 63. Text and music © 1992, Cyprian Consiglio, OSB Cam., and spiritandsong.com®, a division of OCP. All rights reserved.

180

My God, My God

Mark Friedman

Refrain: 1st time: Cantor, All repeat; thereafter: All

My God, my God, why have you a - ban - doned me?

Verses

1. All who see me in - sult me,_____ shake their heads:
2. E - vil ones, they sur - round me_____ like an - gry dogs.
3. They di - vide up my gar - ments,_____ cast - ing lots.
4. I will speak of your name for____ all my days.

1. "He put trust in the Lord, let's see if God
2. They press round me and stare. They pierce my hands,
3. Do not leave me, O Lord. Oh, be my strength,
4. Ja - cob's fam - 'ly, sing praise. Oh, fear the Lord,

to Refrain

1. res - cues him, if he is God's friend."
2. wound my feet, num - ber all my bones.
3. God I pray, quick - ly come to me.
4. praise the Lord, House of Is - ra - el.

181

Song for Veneration of the Cross

Paule Freeburg, DC and Christopher Walker

Cantor, All repeat

Je - sus, I love the cross, I love the cross that set me

free. Je - sus, I love the cross, I

love the cross that lets me live for - ev - er.

Purify My Heart

(Refiner's Fire)

Brian Doerksen

Verses

1. Pu-ri-fy my heart, let me be as gold and pre-cious sil-ver.
2. Pu-ri-fy my heart, cleanse me from with-in and make me ho-ly.

1. Pu - ri - fy my heart, let me be as gold, pure___ gold.
2. Pu - ri - fy my heart, cleanse me from my sin, deep with-in.

Refrain

Re - fin - er's fire, my heart's one de-sire is to be

ho - ly, set a-part for you, Lord. I choose to be

ho - ly, set a-part for you, my mas - ter,

1, Final   **6** to Verse 2   **2** to Refrain

rea-dy to do your will.

183 Show Us Your Mercy

Mark Friedman

Refrain

In times of trou-ble, God, come to our aid. Show us your mer-cy, come save! In times of trou-ble, God, come to our aid. Show us your mer-cy, come save!

1-3 to Verses

save!

Final

Show us your mer-cy, come save!

Verses

1. We live se-cure in the shel-ter of God, safe in the fold of God's wings. We will pro-claim the great-ness of God, the rock of sal-va-tion God brings.
2. Lost and a-fraid, we're nev-er a-lone, God watch-es o-ver our lives. Walk-ing our path and light-ing our way, guard-ing us day and by night.
3. All of our lives we look to our God. We will lie safe in God's care. God is our rock. In God we can trust all of our trou-bles to bear.

to Refrain

The King of Glory

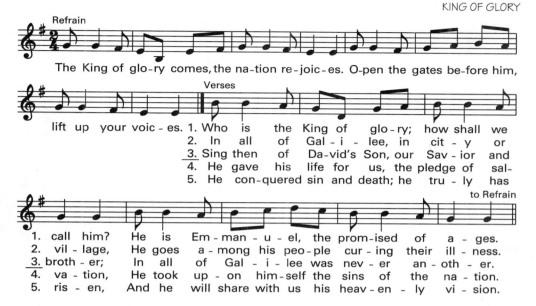

The King of glo-ry comes, the na-tion re-joic-es. O-pen the gates be-fore him, lift up your voic-es.

Verses

1. Who is the King of glo-ry; how shall we
2. In all of Gal-i-lee, in cit-y or
3. Sing then of Da-vid's Son, our Sav-ior and
4. He gave his life for us, the pledge of sal-
5. He con-quered sin and death; he tru-ly has

to Refrain

1. call him? He is Em-man-u-el, the prom-ised of a-ges.
2. vil-lage, He goes a-mong his peo-ple cur-ing their ill-ness.
3. broth-er; In all of Gal-i-lee was nev-er an-oth-er.
4. va-tion, He took up-on him-self the sins of the na-tion.
5. ris-en, And he will share with us his heav-en-ly vi-sion.

Text: 12 12 with refrain. Text © 1967, William F. Jabusch. Administered by OCP. All rights reserved. Music: Trad. Israeli Folk Song.

Were You There

1. Were you there when they crucified my Lord?
   Were you there when they crucified my Lord?
   Oh! Sometimes it causes me to tremble, tremble, tremble.
   Were you there when they crucified my Lord?

2. Were you there when they nailed him to the tree?
   Were you there when they nailed him to the tree?
   Oh! Sometimes it causes me to tremble, tremble, tremble.
   Were you there when they nailed him to the tree?

3. Were you there when they laid him in the tomb?
   Were you there when they laid him in the tomb?
   Oh! Sometimes it causes me to tremble, tremble, tremble.
   Were you there when they laid him in the tomb?

Text: 10 10 14 10. Text and music: Spiritual; *Old Plantation Hymns*, Boston, 1899.

186   Transfigure Us, O Lord

Bob Hurd

Refrain

Trans-fig-ure us, O Lord, trans-fig-ure us, O Lord.

Break the chains that bind us; speak your heal-ing word, and

where you lead we'll fol-low. Trans-fig-ure us, O Lord.

Verses

1. Down from heights of glo-ry in-to the depths be-low, the
2. Light for those in dark-ness, the hun-gry have their fill, glad
3. Par-don for the sin-ner, a shep-herd for the sheep, a
4. To the ho-ly cit-y, Je-ru-sa-lem, you go; your

1. love of God self-emp-tied, the love of God to show. You
2. tid-ings for the hum-ble, the heal-ing of all ills; in
3. drink of liv-ing wa-ter for all who thirst and seek, and
4. face set toward the end-ing, the cross to be your throne.

to Refrain

1. light the path be-fore us, the way that we must go.
2. these we glimpse your glo-ry, God's prom-is-es ful-filled.
3. feast-ing at your ta-ble, the low-ly and the least.
4. Shall we jour-ney with you and share your pas-chal road?

Text: Based on Matthew 17:1–9; Mark 9:2–10; Luke 9:28b–36. Text and music © 2002, Bob Hurd. Published by OCP. All rights reserved.

Lent & Holy Week

What Wondrous Love Is This

WONDROUS LOVE

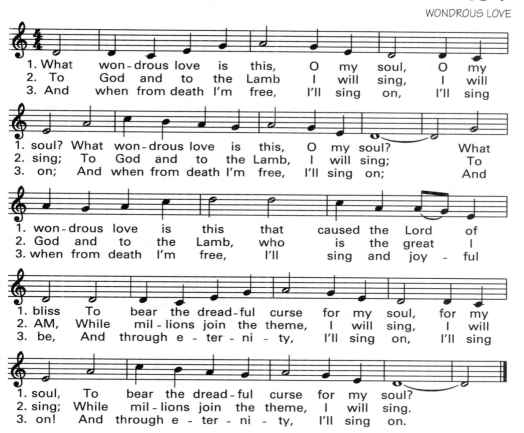

1. What won-drous love is this, O my soul, O my
2. To God and to the Lamb I will sing, I will
3. And when from death I'm free, I'll sing on, I'll sing

1. soul? What won-drous love is this, O my soul? What
2. sing; To God and to the Lamb, I will sing; To
3. on; And when from death I'm free, I'll sing on; And

1. won-drous love is this that caused the Lord of
2. God and to the Lamb, who is the great I
3. when from death I'm free, I'll sing and joy - ful

1. bliss To bear the dread-ful curse for my soul, for my
2. AM, While mil - lions join the theme, I will sing, I will
3. be, And through e - ter - ni - ty, I'll sing on, I'll sing

1. soul, To bear the dread-ful curse for my soul?
2. sing; While mil - lions join the theme, I will sing.
3. on! And through e - ter - ni - ty, I'll sing on.

Text: 12 9 12 12 9; anon.; first appeared in *A General Selection of the Newest and Most Admired Hymns and Spiritual Songs,* 1811, adapt.
Music: William Walker's *The Southern Harmony,* 1835.

Lent & Holy Week

188

Your Only Son
(Lamb of God)

Twila Paris

Verses

1. Your on-ly Son, no sin to hide, but you have
2. Your gift of love they cru-ci-fied, they laughed and
3. I was so lost I should have died, but you have

1. sent him from your side to walk up-on this guilt-y
2. scorned him as he died; the hum-ble King they named a
3. brought me to your side to be led by your staff and

1. sod, and to be-come the Lamb of God.
2. fraud, and sac-ri-ficed the Lamb of God.
3. rod, and to be called a Lamb of God.

Refrain

O Lamb of God, sweet Lamb of God; I love the

ho-ly Lamb of God. O wash me in his pre-cious

blood. My Je-sus Christ, the Lamb of God.

Holy Spirit, Come Now

189

Jesse Manibusan

Refrain

Ho - ly Spir - it, come, Ho - ly Spir - it, come now,

come now.

1. Oh, the sweet-
2. In the faith
3. With the rev -

1. - ness of your mer - cy and grace! Bring us true wis -
2. we share,_____ flow - ing from truth, bring us the knowl -
3. - 'rence of the Lord,__ love is shown. Serv - ing each oth -

1. - dom right here in this place. Bring a glim -
2. - edge that brings us to you. Through the dark -
3. - er, God's pres - ence is known. Oh, the good -

1. - mer of the depth of God's will. Bring un - der - stand -
2. - ness of de - spair and of fear, give us the cour -
3. - ness and the glo - ry of God! Hearts o - ver - flow -

to Refrain

1. - ing; God's plan be ful - filled.
2. - age to know you are here.
3. - ing with won - der and awe.

190

Alleluia Festivalé

Janet Sullivan Whitaker

Verses

Cantor   **All**

1. Je - sus Christ is ris - en to - day,
2. Hymns of praise then let us sing, ——
3. But the pains which he en - dured, ——
4. Sing we to our God a - bove, ——

} Al - le -

1-4. lu - ia, al - le, al - le - lu - ia!

Cantor   **All**

1. our tri - um - phant ho - ly day, ——
2. un - to Christ, our heav - en - ly King,
3. our sal - va - tion have pro - cured, ——
4. praise e - ter - nal as his love, ——

} Al - le -

1-4. lu - ia, al - le, al - le-lu - ia!

Cantor

{ who did once up - on
who en - dured the cross
now a - bove the sky
praise him, all ye heav -

All

1. the cross, ——
2. and grave, ——
3. he's King, ——
4. - en - ly host,

} Al - le - lu - ia, al - le,

Cantor   **All**

1-4. al - le-lu - ia!

{ suf - fer to re - deem our loss.
sin - ners to re - deem and save.
where the an - gels ev - er sing.
Fa - ther, Son, and Ho - ly Ghost.

} Al - le -

1-4. lu - ia, al - le, al - le - lu - ia!

A - men! Ev - 'ry land and peo - ple re - joic - ing!

1-3 · *to Verses 2-4* · 4 · *to Refrain*

A - men! Sing al - le - lu - ia! Sing al - le - lu - ia!

Final

Sing al - le - lu - ia! Sing al - le - lu - ia! Sing al - le - lu - ia!

Text: Latin, 14th cent.; tr. fr. *Lyra Davidica*, 1708, alt.; verse 4, Charles Wesley, 1707–1788.
Music © 1989, 2000, Janèt Sullivan Whitaker. Published by OCP. All rights reserved.

Jesus Christ Is Risen Today   **191**

EASTER HYMN

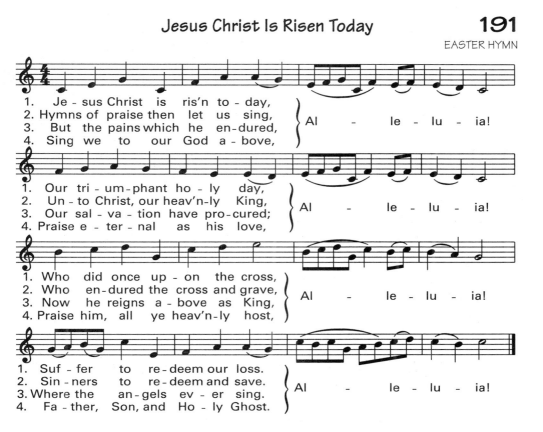

1. Je - sus Christ is ris'n to - day,
2. Hymns of praise then let us sing,
3. But the pains which he en - dured,
4. Sing we to our God a - bove,

Al - le - lu - ia!

1. Our tri - um - phant ho - ly day,
2. Un - to Christ, our heav'n - ly King,
3. Our sal - va - tion have pro - cured;
4. Praise e - ter - nal as his love,

Al - le - lu - ia!

1. Who did once up - on the cross,
2. Who en - dured the cross and grave,
3. Now he reigns a - bove as King,
4. Praise him, all ye heav'n - ly host,

Al - le - lu - ia!

1. Suf - fer to re - deem our loss.
2. Sin - ners to re - deem and save.
3. Where the an - gels ev - er sing.
4. Fa - ther, Son, and Ho - ly Ghost.

Al - le - lu - ia!

Text: 77 77 with alleluias; verse 1, Latin, 14th cent.; para. in *Lyra Davidica*, 1708, alt.; verses 2–3, *The Compleat Psalmodist*, ca. 1750, alt.;
verse 4, Charles Wesley, 1707–1788, alt. Music: Later form of melody fr. *Lyra Davidica*, 1708.

192

Come, Holy Ghost

Based on LAMBILOTTE
Arranged by Sarah Hart and Kevin B. Hipp

Verse 1

1. Come, Ho - ly Ghost, Cre - a - tor blest, And in our
1. hearts take up thy rest; Come with thy grace and
1. heav'n - ly aid To fill the hearts which thou hast made,
1. To fill the hearts which thou hast made.

Verse 2

2. O Com - fort - er, to thee we cry, Thou heav'n - ly gift of
2. God most high; Thou font of life, and fire of love,
2. And sweet a - noint - ing from a - bove, And sweet a - noint - ing
2. from a - bove.

Bridge

Verse 3

3. Praise be to thee, Fa-ther and Son And Ho-ly Spir - it,

3. with them one; and may the Son on us be -

3. stow The gifts that from the Spir - it flow,

3. The gifts that from the Spir - it flow.

Text: *Veni, Creator Spiritus*; attr. to Rabanus Maurus, 776–856, tr. by Edward Caswall, 1814–1878, alt.
Arrangement © 2001, 2002, Sarah Hart (used with permission of Music Services, Inc. All rights reserved.) and Kevin B. Hipp.
Published by spiritandsong.com®, a division of OCP. All rights reserved.

193

Holy, Holy, Holy Cry

Rick Modlin

Verses

1. The Lamb of God stands on the height
2. In bit-ter sac-ri-fice once slain,
3. To him now let our prayers a-rise
4. While heav-ens' prais-es hail his worth,

1. a-mong the glor-ious clouds of light,
2. he lives in tri-umph there to reign
3. in clouds of in-cense to the skies,
4. he catch-es up the prayers of earth

1. a-bove the cit-y paved in gold
2. a-mong the saints clad all in white
3. from cen-ser borne by an-gel hands,
4. in wound-ed hands, till, count-less throng,

[1 to Verse 2]

1. where death and dark-ness have no hold.
2. in realms where day yields not to night.
3. bright tongues of fire from far-flung lands.
4. the sing-ers come to join the song.

[2-4] **Refrain**

And, "Ho-ly, ho-ly, ho-ly" cry to you,

our Lord Most High. "Ho-ly, ho-ly, ho-ly" cry

[1, 2, Final | to Verses 3, 4]
3 (Fine)

to you, our God Most High.

3 Bridge

Soloist To Fa - ther, Son, and Spir - it, Three High.

Choir/All To Fa - ther, Son, in One all - ho - ly Mys - ter - y.

and Spir - it, Three

To Fa - ther, Son, in One all - ho - ly Mys - ter - y.

and Spir - it, Three in One all - ho -

- ly Mys - ter - y.

to Refrain
All
And,

Text: Genevieve Glen, OSB, © 1998, 2001, The Benedictine Nuns of the Abbey of St. Walburga. Music © 2004, Rick Modlin. Published by OCP. All rights reserved.

194   Lord of the Dance

SHAKER SONG

Verses

1. I danced in the morn-ing when the world was be-gun, And I
2. I danced for the scribe __ and the Phar - i - see, But they
3. I danced on the Sab-bath and I cured the __ lame, The __
4. I danced on a Fri-day when the sky turned _ black; It's __
5. They cut me __ down __ and I leapt up __ high, _____

1. danced in the moon and the stars __ and the sun, And I
2. would not __ dance and they would-n't fol - low me; I ____
3. ho - ly ____ peo - ple, they said it was a shame; They ____
4. hard to __ dance with the dev - il on your back; They ____
5. I am the life that - 'll nev - er, nev - er die, I'll ____

1. came down from heav-en and I danced on the earth, ___ At
2. danced for the fish - er-men, for James and for John; ___ They
3. whipped and they stripped _ and they hung me __ high, And they
4. bur - ied my bod - y and they thought I'd __ gone, ___ But
5. live in ____ you __ if you'll live in ___ me;

Refrain

1. Beth - le - hem I ____ had my birth. "Dance, then wher-
2. came with __ me and the dance went on.
3. left me __ there on a cross to die.
4. I am the dance and I still go on.
5. "I am the Lord of the Dance," said he.

ev-er you may be. I am the Lord of the Dance," said he. "I'll

lead you all wher-ev-er you may be, I will lead you all in the

1-4

Dance," said he.

to Verses   **Final**

Dance," said he.

Text: Irregular with refrain; Sydney B. Carter, 1915–2004. Music: Shaker Melody, 19th cent.; adapt. by Sydney B. Carter.
Text and music © 1963, Stainer & Bell Ltd., London, England. All rights reserved. Administered by Hope Publishing Co. Used with permission.

Easter/Pentecost

Nadie en el Sepulcro/No One in the Tomb

Jaime Cortez

Estribillo: La primera vez: Solista, Todos repiten; después: Todos
Refrain: 1st time: Cantor, All repeat; thereafter: All

Al - le - lu - ia!   ¡A - le - lu - ya!

Verse 1a: 1st time: Cantor; All repeat
Estrofa 1b: La primera vez: Solista; Todos repiten

1a. This is the day   that the Lord   has made;
1b. És-te es el dí - a en que ac-tuó el Se - ñor;

al Estribillo
to Refrain
2

1a. let us re-joice and be glad.
1b. nues-tro es el go - zo y la a - le - grí - a.

Estrofa 2a: La primera vez: Solista; Todos repiten
Verse 2b: 1st time: Cantor; All repeat

2a. Cris - to nues-tra vi - da, _____
2b. We who dwell with Christ in God ___

al Estribillo
to Refrain
2

2a. Cris - to nues-tra glo - ria.
2b. live with him in glo - ry.

Estrofa 3 (siga la dirección del Solista)
Verse 3 (follow Cantor's direction)

al Estribillo
to Refrain

3. Na-die en el se-pul - cro. No one in the tomb.

Text: Based on Psalm 118:24; 1 Samuel 3:10; John 6:35; English verse 1 © 1969, 1981, ICEL. All rights reserved. Used with permission.
Spanish verses 1 & 3 © 1970, Comisión Episcopal Española de Liturgia. All rights reserved. Used with permission.
Music and English verses 2 & 3, and Spanish verse 2 © 1997, Jaime Cortez. Published by OCP. All rights reserved.

Note: Gospel verses found in accompaniment books.

Easter/Pentecost

196

Now Is the Time

Tom Kendzia

Refrain

Come to us, you who say, "I will not for-get you." Be with us, you
who say, "Do not be a-fraid." Take hold of us, our hearts, our
minds, our whole be - ing. Make us your own, now is the time.

Verses

Cantor / *All*

1. Spir-it of love, crush the pain of ha - tred.
2. Spir-it of peace, si - lence tongues of an - ger.
3. Spir-it of faith, rise a - bove our doubt - ing.

Cantor / *All* / *Cantor*

1. Spir-it of hope, stand be - fore our eyes. Spir-it of light,
2. Spir-it of life, break the chains of death. Spir-it of joy,
3. Spir-it of truth, save us from our lies. Spir-it of God,

All / *to Refrain*

1. dance with - in our dark-ness. Make us your own, now is the time.
2. o - ver-come our sad-ness. Make us your own, now is the time.
3. walk a-mong your peo-ple. Make us your own, now is the time.

*Last time, repeat final phrase twice.

Easter/Pentecost

Rise Up with Him

197

Janet Vogt

Verses

1. Peo-ple, wait no more. God has shown you _____
2. Ev-'ry knee shall bend. Ev-'ry tongue con-fess __
3. Je-sus, whom we love, we pro-claim your word __

1. _____ the glo-ry of the Lord! By the cross we
2. _____ that Je-sus Christ is Lord, Lord and Sav-ior
3. _____ for ag-es all to come. Al-le-lu-ia,

1. claim our free-dom. Christ has ris-en _____ to
2. of all na-tions, our sal-va-tion _____ to
3. sing a new song. Glo-ry to our God _____ of

1-3. ev-er-last-ing life!

Refrain

And we'll rise up, rise up with him, and we'll rise, rise to new life! And we'll rise up, rise up with him, for with

1, 2

Je-sus who leads us by grace we will rise up with him.

to Verses 2, 3 ‖ **Final**

2

For with Je-sus who leads us by grace we will rise up with him.

Text: Based on Philippians 2:1–11; 1 Corinthians 15:20–26. Text and music © 1996, Janet Vogt. Published by OCP. All rights reserved.

Easter/Pentecost

198

Song of the Cross

Susan HooKong-Taylor

Refrain

Love lift-ed on the cross for me: my Lord, my God, my sal -

va - tion. Love lift-ed high to set me free: my

Lord, my God, my sal - va - tion. va - tion. *to Verses*

va - tion. va - tion.

Verses

1. Be - hold the wood of the cross, _____
2. O be ex - alt - ed, O God, _____
3. Give glo - ry to the ____ Fa - ther,

1. be - hold the lamb ____ that was slain.
2. a - bove the heav - ens and the earth.
3. give glo - ry to ____ the ____ Son,

1. Be - hold your king ____ comes vic - to - ri - ous,
2. For by your cross and res - ur - rec - tion
3. give glo - ry to the Ho - ly Spir - it;

to Refrain

1. be - hold he has ris - en a - gain.
2. you have re - deemed _____ the world.
3. give glo - ry ____ to the Ho - ly One.

Spirit, Come Down

Janet Vogt and Mark Friedman

Refrain Spir - it, Spir - it, Spir - it,

Verses 1. Breath of life, breath of life, breath of life,
2. Fire of love, fire of love, fire of love,
3. *Spi - ri - tus,* *Spi - ri - tus,* *Spi - ri - tus,*

Ref. come down from heav - en. Spir - it,

1-3. come down from heav - en. Breath of life,
Fire of love,
Spi - ri - tus,

As needed | Final

Ref. Spir - it, and seal us with your love. love. And

1. breath of life,
2. fire of love, and seal us with your love.
3. *Spi - ri - tus,*

seal us with your love. And seal us with your love.

200 Worthy Is the Lamb

Ricky Manalo

Refrain

Wor-thy is the Lamb that was slain to re - ceive hon-or and glo - ry. Wor-thy are the ones who be - lieve to re - ceive the good-ness of God.

Verses

1. Wor - thy are you, O Pas - chal Lamb.
2. Wor - thy are you, O Bread of Life. Sal -
3. Wor - thy are you, O Ris - en Christ.

1. Wis - dom and strength be - long now to you. You
2. va - tion and joy be - long now to us. By
3. Won - ders and signs, re - veal - ing your might. Your

1. laid down your life and died up - on the cross: we've be -
2. con - quer - ing death and ris - ing to new life, we've be -
3. pow - er and glo - ry shine up - on our lives: we've be -

2 to Refrain

1. come a peo - ple of hope.
2. come a peo - ple of praise.
3. come your light for the world.

Text: Based on Revelation 5:9–14. Text and music © 1997, Ricky Manalo, CSP. Published by spiritandsong.com®, a division of OCP. All rights reserved.

Holy Is His Name

201

John Michael Talbot

Marian Music/May Crowning

202 Hail Mary: Gentle Woman

Carey Landry
Arranged by Sarah Hart

Hail Ma-ry, full of grace, the Lord is with you. Bless-ed are you a-mong wom-en and blest is the fruit of your womb, Je - sus. Ho-ly Ma - ry, Moth-er of God, oh, pray for us sin - ners now and at the hour of death. A - men.

Refrain

Gen-tle wom-an, qui-et light, morn-ing star, so strong and bright, gen-tle Moth-er, peace-ful dove, teach us wis-dom; teach us love. Oh, teach us love. A-ve, a-ve, Ma - rí - a.

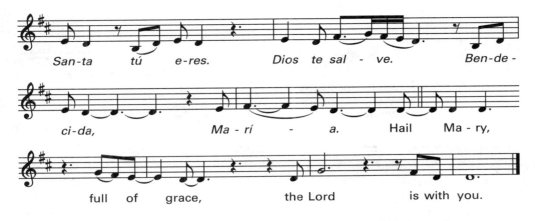

Santa tú e-res. Dios te sal - ve. Ben-de-

ci-da, Ma - rí - a. Hail Ma - ry,

full of grace, the Lord is with you.

Immaculate Mary

203

LOURDES HYMN

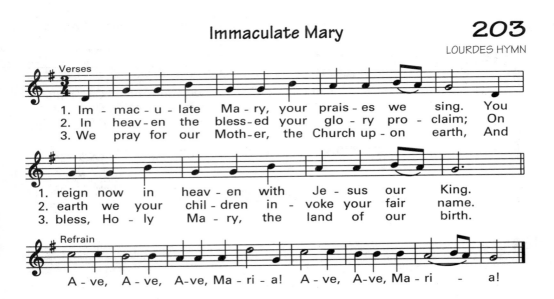

Verses

1. Im - mac - u - late Ma - ry, your prais - es we sing. You
2. In heav - en the bless - ed your glo - ry pro - claim; On
3. We pray for our Moth - er, the Church up - on earth, And

1. reign now in heav - en with Je - sus our King.
2. earth we your chil - dren in - voke your fair name.
3. bless, Ho - ly Ma - ry, the land of our birth.

Refrain

A - ve, A - ve, A - ve, Ma - ri - a! A - ve, A - ve, Ma - ri - a!

Text: 11 11 with refrain; anon. in *Parochial Hymn Book*, Boston, 1897; rev. of *Hail Virgin of virgins* by Jeremiah Cummings, 1814–1866, alt.
Music: trad. Pyrenean Melody; pub. Grenoble, 1882; alt. by Augustus Edmonds Tozer, 1857–1910.

204   Let It Be Done

Chris Muglia

Verses

1. When she heard the voice of God
2. When he heard the voice of God
3. When we hear the voice of God

1. calling her to be the in-stru-ment he need-
2. calling him to stand and take the vir-gin as his wife
3. calling out our names, Lord, we pray you give us faith

1. -ed to bring our world the King of Kings, she
2. and teach her child to be a man, he
3. to an-swer you in an-y-thing. And we

1. could not un-der-stand the wis-dom of God's plan,
2. could not un-der-stand the wis-dom of God's plan,
3. may not un-der-stand the wis-dom of your plan,

1. but still she an-swered: "Let it be.
2. but still he an-swered: "Let it be.
3. but we will an-swer: "Let it be.

1. Let it be done un-to me." (to Verse 2)
2. Let it be done un-to me." (to Refrain)
3. Let it be done un-to me." (to Refrain)

Refrain

And we say: "Yes, Lord, we're read-y to re-ceive.

Yes, Lord, we're read-y to be-lieve. Let it be.

Marian Music/May Crowning

Let it be done un-to me."

to Verse 3 (Fine)

And we say:

Holy Mary

205

Mark Friedman and Janet Vogt

Refrain

Ho-ly Ma-ry, we come to hon-or you. We crown you this day,

the queen of our hearts. Ma - ry, you are filled with the

Lord's own grace. Sal - ve, Re-gi-na, Ho-ly Ma-ry. Ho-ly Ma-ry.

1-3 to Verses | Final

Sal - ve, Re-gi - na, Ho-ly Ma - ry.

Verses
All   Cantor   All

1. We crown you this day   the moth-er of our sav-ior.   You
2. We crown you this day   the vir-gin blest and cho-sen.   The
3. We crown you this day   the vir-gin pure and ho-ly,   our

to Refrain

1. show us the way to Je - sus Christ our Lord.
2. gift of your life has shown us how to love.
3. help when we cry out to you in prayer.

206

My Soul Rejoices

Jackie Francois

Refrain

My soul re - joic - es, my soul re - joic - es in my God.

Verses

1. My
2. The

1. soul__ pro - claims__ the great - ness of the Lord; my
2. Al - might - y has_____ done great things for me and

1. spir - it re - joic - es in God my Sav - ior;
2. ho - ly_____ is his name._____

1. he has looked__ up - on his low - ly ser - vant and
2. He has mer - cy on those who fear him,

to Refrain

1. all gen - er - a - tions will call me bless - ed.
2. those__ in ev - 'ry gen - er - a - tion.

O Sanctissima
(O Most Holy One)

207

O DU FRÖHLICHE
Magnificat by Ken Canedo

1, 5. O Sanc - tís - si - ma, Ho - ly Queen of Love,
2. O most beau - ti - ful, And most mer - ci - ful,
3. Ma - ry, Mys - tic Rose, Font that o - ver-flows,
4. Ma - ry, plead for us; In - ter - cede for us.

1, 5. Dear - est Vir - gin and Moth - er.
2. Gate of Heav - en, we hail you.
3. Seat of Wis - dom, we greet you.
4. Come and lead us to Je - sus.

1, 5. Blest by ev - 'ry na - tion, Ev - 'ry gen - er - a - tion:
2. Star of our sal - va - tion, Crown of all cre - a - tion:
3. Moth - er of our Sav - ior, Full of grace and fa - vor:
4. Moth - er in our sad - ness, Moth - er in our glad - ness:

1, 3, Final

1-5. O - ra, o - ra pro no - bis!

2, 4 Magnificat

1. My soul pro-claims the great-ness of the Lord. My _
4. He has come to help his ser - vant, Is - ra - el. He re -

1 to Hymn Vs. 3 | 2 to Hymn Vs. 5

1. spir - it finds joy in God my Sav - ior.
4. mem-bers his prom-is - es to A-bra-ham.

Magnificat Verses 2, 3: sung by the choir over Hymn Verses 3, 4

2. God looks with favor on his lowly servant,
   and from this day all will call me blest.
   Great things he's done for me.
   His name is holy.
   Mercy, mercy on God's people.

3. He has shown power, he has cast down the mighty.
   He has lifted the lowly.
   He feeds the hungry.
   The rich go empty.
   Mercy, mercy on God's people.

Text: Hymn: 55 7 D; English tr. of O Sanctissima by Harry Hagan, OSB, © 2003, St. Meinrad Archabbey. Magnificat adapt. by Ken Canedo.
Magnificat text and music © 2006, Ken Canedo. Published by OCP. All rights reserved.

Marian Music/May Crowning

208 Salve, Regina (A Litany to Mary)

Salve Regina, Chant, Mode V
Arranged by Mark Friedman and Janet Vogt

Section 1

Sal - ve, Re - gí - na, Ma - ter mi - se - ri - cór - di - ae:

Vi - ta dul - cé - do et spes no - stra, sal - ve. Hail, Queen of heav - en,

our Moth - er, kind and mer - ci - ful: Pray for your chil - dren.

Section 2

Ho - ly Ma - ry, pray for us.

Hail, our sweet-ness and our hope.

(sing 7 times)

Section 3

Ho - ly Ma - ry, pray for us. 1. Ma - ry, lead us to your Son,
2. Ma - ry, Moth - er of the Church,

1. Je - sus, bro - ther, Ho - ly One. Ho - ly Ma - ry, filled with grace,
2. bring your peace to all on earth. Com - fort all who go a - stray,

[1] (sing 6 times) to Section 3

1. in your life we see God's face. Ho - ly Ma - ry, pray for us.
2. lead us in your guid - ing way.

[2] **Section 4** (sing 10 times) to Section 5 **Section 5**

Ho - ly Ma - ry, pray for us. Sal - ve, Re - gí - na, Ma - ter mi - se - ri -

cór - di - ae: Vi - ta dul - cé - do et spes no - stra, sal - ve.

Hail, Queen of heav - en, our Moth-er, kind and mer - ci - ful:

Pray for your chil-dren. Hail, our sweet-ness and our hope.

Ho - ly Ma - ry, pray for us. Ho - ly Ma - ry, pray for us.

Ho - ly Ma - ry, pray for us. Ho - ly Ma - ry, pray for

Section 6

us. Vi - ta dul-cé - do et spes no-stra, sal - ve.

Father, I Give Myself
(Prayer of Abandonment)

Tom Booth

Verse 1
1. Fa-ther, I give my-self to you. Do with me as you
1. will, for what-ev-er you do, I thank you;
1. I am read-y for all.

Verse 2
2. Let on-ly your will be done in me
2. as is done in your cre-a - tion; I ask noth-ing
2. else. Ah, ah.
Ah, ah.

Verse 3
3. Fa-ther, I sur-ren-der; I place my-self in your hands
3. be - cause you are my fa - ther
3. and be-cause I love you; in - to your
3. hands I com-mend my spir - it.

Graduation/End of Year

Friends for Life

Bob Halligan Jr.

Refrain

Lord, I know that you and I are friends for life. I know you al-ways will be there. Lord, I know that

1, 2: to Verses
3: to Bridge
4: to Refrain

you and I are friends for life, not just this life.

Verses

1. Ev - 'ry-bod-y's think - in' of heav - en as far a - way, but
2. Some of my ___ friends ___ in this world have let me down.

1. heav - en - ly love and friend - ship are here to - day.
2. Lord, ___ I see you al - ways will be a - round.

1. I don't have to be lone - ly; I don't have to be
2. I don't have to be an - gry; I don't have to be

to Refrain

1. wor - ried. I can tru - ly say:
2. hur - ried, 'cause you lead the way.

Bridge

You are so good to me. I love you end - less - ly.

to Refrain

Thank you, thank you, Lord.

Graduation/End of Year

211

Peace, My Friend

Jaime Rickert

Verse 1

1. When the time has come for leav - ing, when the words have all

1. been spo - ken, when you know the door is o - pen as it

1. al - ways will re - main. When the last good-bye has ech - oed,

1. when the last tear has been shed, when we've said it all

1. a hun - dred times, we'll say it once a - gain.

Refrain

Peace, my friend, may the love of God go with you. May the

Fa - ther guide your foot - steps. May the sun shine ev - 'ry day.

Peace, my friend, may the Spir-it walk be - side you. May his

grace be warm with - in you. May you al - ways find your way.

1   2   to Verse 2   ‖ Final

May the Fa - ther guide

your foot - steps. May you al - ways find your way.

Note: As recorded, verses 1 and 2 are performed in reverse order.

Graduation/End of Year

Verse 2

2. We have come to know each oth - er. We have come to love

2. each oth - er. We are more when we're to-geth - er than we

2. are when we're a-part. Though the years may fall be-tween us,

2. we must nev - er fear the dis - tance. We are one in God

to Refrain

2. for-ev - er in our minds and in our hearts.

Walk On with Jesus

Mark Friedman and Janet Vogt

Verses

1. The road leads from fear through our un-rav-eled
2. Do you fath-om the mean-ing of the sto-ries you've
3. In the midst of our jour-ney, when we most crave a

1. lives. When the cross looms a-bove us, our hop-ing sur-
2. heard? Have you o-pened your hearts so to wel-come my
3. rest, when our hun-ger is great-est, with our spir-its dis-

1. vives. As the voice of the strang-er we _ meet on the
2. word? The one who was prom-ised had to car-ry the
3. tressed, we _ beg him to join us at the ta-ble we

1. way _____ com-pels us and tells us how his
2. cross so the world would know tri-umph out of
3. share; in the strang-er we wel-come, find a

1st time: to Verse 2

1. love won the day.
2. suf-f'ring and loss.
3. new way to care.

Refrain

And we walk on with Je-sus with a liv-ing

faith, with a faith that is bold, with a

faith that bears fruit as the sto-ry we share is re-told.

1, Final
(Fine)

And we walk on with Je-sus.

Graduation/End of Year

And we walk on with Je - sus.

Bridge

The act of our shar - ing, the bread that we break, helps our hopes to re - kin - dle, lets the fi - re a - wake. And our hearts burn with - in us. We know it's the Lord.

Sing 3 times

He has nour - ished our faith and our spir - its re - stored, nour - ished our faith and our spir - its re - stored.

213   Be Not Afraid

Bob Dufford, SJ

Verse 1

1. You shall cross the bar-ren des-ert, but you shall not die of
1. thirst. You shall wan-der far in safe-ty though you do not know the
1. way. You shall speak your words in for-eign lands and all will un-der-
1. stand. You shall see the face of God and live.

Refrain

Be not a-fraid. I go be-fore you al-ways. Come fol-low
me, and I will give you rest.

1, 2 — to Vss 2, 3 | Final 2

Verse 2

2. If you pass through rag-ing wa-ters in the sea, you shall not
2. drown. If you walk a-mid the burn-ing flames, you shall not be
2. harmed. If you stand be-fore the pow'r of hell and death is at your
2. side, know that I am with you through it all.

Reconciliation

Verse 3

3. Bless-ed are your poor, for the king-dom shall be theirs. Blest are you that

3. weep and mourn, for one day you shall laugh. And if wick-ed tongues in-sult and

to Refrain

3. hate you all be-cause of me, bless-ed, bless-ed are you!

Amazing Grace

214

NEW BRITAIN

1. A - maz - ing grace! How sweet the sound That saved a
   Alternate text: (and
2. 'Twas grace that taught my heart to fear, And grace my
3. Through man - y dan - gers, toils, and snares I have al -
4. The Lord has prom - ised good to me, His word my
5. When we've been there ten thou - sand years, Bright shin - ing

1. wretch like me! I once was lost, but
   set me free!)
2. fears re - lieved; How pre - cious did that
3. read - y come; 'Tis grace has brought me
4. hope se - cures; He will my shield and
5. as the sun, We've no less days to

1. now am found, Was blind but now I see.
2. grace ap - pear The hour I first be - lieved!
3. safe thus far, And grace will lead me home.
4. por - tion be As long as life en - dures.
5. sing God's praise Than when we first be - gun.

Reconciliation

215

By Your Touch

Jaime Rickert

Refrain

By your touch we are made whole. By your love we are for-giv - en.

By your Spir - it we are born to live for-ev - er.

1. to Refrain

2, 3 - er. *4* to Verses Final - er.

Verse 1

1. Je - sus, will you hear me when I call u-pon your name,

1. for I am help - less, and I am wound-ed in my heart.

1. Stand - ing in the dark - ness now, I

1. lis-ten for your call. I am a - fraid to walk with-out

to Refrain

1. you, a - fraid to start a - gain.

Reconciliation

Verse 2

2. In the weak-ness of temp-ta - tion, and in the si-lence of de-spair

2. I have been bro - ken, but I will rise to stand a - gain.

2. You give love with-out a turn - ing point,

2. life with-out an end, the cour-age to be faith-

to Refrain

2. - ful and the light that fills the soul.

216

Be with Me, Lord

Refrain: Trad., arr. by Tom Booth
Verses: Tom Booth

Refrain

Be with me, Lord. Be with me, my Lord. When I'm in trou-ble and I don't know where to go, be with me, Lord.

Verse 1

1. When I'm blind, when I can-not see, when all life's trou-ble sweeps o - ver me, when I'm in dark-ness and all I see is me, be with me, Lord.

to Refrain

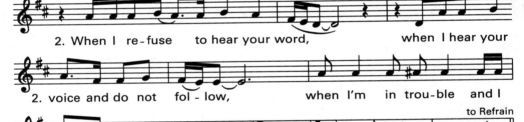

Verse 2

2. When I re-fuse to hear your word, when I hear your voice and do not fol - low, when I'm in trou-ble and I don't know where to go, be with me, Lord.

to Refrain

Reconciliation

Fly Like a Bird

Ken Canedo

Refrain

Fly like a bird to the Lord, my soul.

I want to soar like an ea - gle.

Though I may jour - ney far a - way from home,

I know I'll nev - er be a - lone.

Verses

1. O God, you know who I am.
2. Where can I run from your love?
3. When I am down and a - fraid,

1. You know my hopes and my dreams. In my
2. Where can I hide from my God? From the
3. when I am fall - ing a - way, you ex -

1. pon - der - ing and fears, in my joy and in my tears,
2. dawn of morn - ing's light to the dark - ness of the night,
3. tend a gen - tle hand, and I know you un - der - stand.

to Refrain

1-3. O God, your pres - ence is real.

Reconciliation

218 Give Us Clean Hands

Charlie Hall

Verse

We bow our hearts, we bend our knees; O Spir-it,

come make us hum - ble. We turn our eyes

from e - vil things; O Lord, we cast down our i - dols.

Refrain

Give us clean hands, give us pure hearts; let us not lift our souls

1. to an-oth - er.
2. - er. Give us clean hands.

to Verse 3

Final

- er. O God, let us be a gen - er - a - tion that seeks,

that seeks your face, O God of Ja -

1. - cob. O
2. - cob. Give us clean hands.

Reconciliation

In This Reconciliation

Janet Vogt

Verses

1, 3. By the grace— of for-give-ness, by the wis-dom of your truth,
2. Though not wor-thy to re-ceive you, you re-ceive us as your own.

1, 3. by the com-fort of your pres-ence, we shall learn to fol-low you.
2. Though we wan-der far a - way from you, you al-ways call us home.

1, 3. In this rec - on - cil - i - a - tion, may our lives be made a - new.
2. In this mo-ment of for-give-ness, you have made your love be known.

1
2 to Refrain

1-3. Grant us peace, ho - ly Lord, grant us peace. 2. peace.

Final

3. peace. Grant us peace, ho - ly Lord, grant us peace.

Refrain

For - give us, Lord. For - give us, Lord.

For - give our sins, for - give our deeds.

For - give our words, for - give our hearts.

1
2 to Verse 3

With love out-poured, for-give us, Lord. Lord.

Jesus, My Everything

Matt Maher

Verses

1. I've been look-ing for a rea - son, __
2. Lord, I get so tired _____

1. I've been long-ing for a pur - pose, __
2. of the strug - gle with-in. _____

1. I'm los-ing all my mean - ing, _____
2. I set - tle in com-pla - cen-cy ___ and I'm

1. I've run out of ex - cus - es.
2. weighed down in my sin.

1. Lord, it's hard to know you,
2. So lead me past e - mo - tion,

1. I don't al - ways see your plan.
2. 'cause they change ___ with the wind.

1. But ho - li - ness _____ is call - ing me ___ so
2. I want to be a true dis-ci - ple; _____ to

Refrain

1. take me as I am.
2. dai - ly choose your hand.   'Cause you are my ev -

Reconciliation

-'ry - thing, you are the song I sing; I'll do an -

- y - thing for you. Teach me how

to pray, to live a life of grace; I'll go an -

1

- y - where with you. Je - sus, be my

to Verse 2 2
3

ev - 'ry - thing. You are my ev -

Final

Je - sus, be my ev - 'ry - thing.

Je - sus, be my ev - 'ry - thing.

221   Nothing Is Beyond You

Rich Mullins, Tom Booth and Mitch McVicker

1. Where could I go, where could I run,
1. e-ven if I found the strength to fly?
1. And if I rose on the wings of the dawn
1. and crashed through the cor-ner of the sky,
1. and if I sailed past the edge of the sea, e-ven
1. if I made my bed in hell, still there you would find me.

Noth-ing is be-yond you; you stand be-yond the reach of our vain i-mag - i - na - tions, our mis-guid-ed pi - e-ties. The heav-ens stretch to hold you, and deep cries out to deep, say-ing, "Noth-ing is be-yond you, noth-ing is be-yond you." Time can-not con-tain you, you fill e-ter - ni-ty, and

Reconciliation

sin can nev - er stain you, death has lost its sting. And

I can-not ex - plain the way you came to love me,

ex-cept to say that noth-ing is be-yond you,

1   **7** to Verse 2

noth-ing is be-yond you.

Final

say-ing noth - ing is be-yond you.

Verse 2

2. If I should shrink back from the light

2. so I can sink in - to the dark,

2. if I take cov - er and I close my eyes,

2. e - ven then you would see my heart,

2. and you'd cut through all my pain and rage.

2. For the dark-ness is not dark

to Refrain

2. to you, and night's as bright as day.

Reconciliation

222 Sweet Redeemer

Steve Angrisano and Sarah Hart

Verses

1. King of Kings, bless-ed Je - sus, hand of mer -
2. I was lost and you found me; in the dark -

1. - cy, giv - er of grace; I have
2. - ness, you were my light. When I fell

1. come to sing glo - ry, to lay my heart
2. down, you for - gave me, lift - ed me up

1. be - fore you in this place.
2. and held me to your side.

Refrain

Sweet re - deem - er, I sur - ren - der all I am to you.

Sweet re - deem - er, I sur - ren - der all I am to

1, 2 — 1: to Verse 2 / 2: to Bridge   3 — to Refrain   4, Final — to Refrain (Fine)

you.   you.   you.

Bridge

From the shad - ows of the tomb you called me, you rolled

a - way the stone. From the bur - den of my sin you saved

me, you made my heart your home.   to Refrain

Reconciliation

The Lord Is Kind and Merciful

223

Tom Booth

Refrain

The Lord is kind and mer-ci-ful. The Lord is slow to an - ger and rich in com-pas - sion.

1 The Lord is kind and mer-ci-ful.

2 *to Verses*

Final The Lord is kind and mer - ci-ful.

The Lord is kind and mer - ci - ful.

Verse 1

1. Bless the Lord, O my soul; bless his ho - ly name.

1. Bless the Lord, O my soul, for-get-ting not his ben - e-fits,

to Refrain

1. for-get-ting not his ben - e-fits.

Verse 2

2. As the heav-ens are a-bove the earth, great is God's kind-ness towards us.

2. As the east is far from the west, he has put our

to Refrain

2. sin from us, he has put our sin a-way from us.

Reconciliation

224   You Know Who I Am

Matt Maher and Tom Booth

Verse 1

1. Lord, hear me; I am o-pen, I sur-ren-der all my

1. sin. All my pride gets me no-where, leaves me strand-ed, emp-ty

1. hand-ed. 1-2. So shat-ter the dark-ness in my life

1-2. as I car-ry this cross both day and night all the way,

1-2. *all the way,* all the way, *all the way* to heav-en.

Refrain

You know who I am. Lord, please take my hand and lead me in-

-to com-mu-ni-ty. You know who I am. Lord, help me to stand

1st: to Verse 2
2nd: to Coda

fall-ing in love with your fam-i-ly.

Verse 2

2. I con - fess to you, Je - sus, and to
2. you, my broth-ers and sis-ters, that I have sinned and need for-
2. give-ness. Pray for me, and I for you.

Coda

All the way, *all the way,* all the way, *all the way*
to heav - en. All the way, *all the way,*
all the way, *all the way* to heav - en.

225   Bread of Life

Bobby Fisher

1. Bread of life and cup of hope, we come as gift to
2. Lov-ing Lord, Cre - a - tor God, o - pen our eyes to
3. Liv - ing Word, O Son of God, your love shows us the

1. you.   Change our hearts; fill us with peace. Trans-form our
2. see the good that lives in each of us, that called the
3. way that we may live in har - mo - ny, and from you

1. lives a - new. O - pen our eyes so that we might see
2. world to be. And when we fail to ___ see the good,
3. nev - er stray. Wipe all op - pres-sion _ from our midst;

1. your pres - ence in one an - oth - er. Your life, poured out in
2. when friend-ships fal - ter and crum-ble, give us the cour - age
3. give us a love for all peo - ple. Your song of jus - tice

(Fine) **4**

1. love to - day, u - nites us all in you.
2. to for-give that we may live in peace.
3. sing in us, to live for peace to - day.

Gather at This Feast

226

Mark Friedman and Janet Vogt

Refrain: 1st time: Cantor; thereafter: All

With fam-i-ly and friends we share the bread and wine, a sign of God's
gen-tle love that calls to us to gath-er at this feast. feast.

1, Final — to Refrain
2-7 to Verses, Last time to Refrain

Verses

1. This bread of life, this cup of peace u-
2. We thank you for this ho-ly day. We
3. By your love this bread be-comes your
4. For in this bread we know his love, made
5. With grate-ful hearts and joy we come to

1. nites us in this ho-ly feast, now pres-ent in the
2. call your name, we sing your praise, for Je-sus in his
3. bod-y bro-ken now for us, and by your grace this
4. pres-ent now in all of us, and in this cup we
5. share this bread, to drink this cup, so we may go and

to Refrain

1. love we seek that brings us here this day.
2. kind-ness gave this Eu-cha-rist for all.
3. sav-ing cup is poured for all the world.
4. now are one, one fam-i-ly of faith.
5. be his love, a light for all the world.

Eucharist

227

Jesus Is with Us

Owen Alstott

Refrain

Je-sus is with us to-day, be-side us to guide us to-

day. Je-sus teach-es us, Je-sus heals us, for we are his

Church; we are his cho-sen; we are the chil-dren of God.

Verses

1. Je-sus teach-es us to love one an-oth-er, to care for our
2. Je-sus heals us, he casts out our sad-ness. He comes and
3. Je-sus calls to us, he wants us to know him here in the

1. broth-ers and sis-ters in need. For when we show
2. fills ev-'ry heart with a song. In time of need,
3. scrip-ture and in Eu-cha-rist. For where his friends are

to Refrain

1. kind-ness to oth-ers, we are God's chil-dren in-deed.
2. he walks be-side us, Je-sus to whom we be-long.
3. gath-ered to-geth-er, Je-sus is there in their midst.

Jesus, You Are Bread for Us

Christopher Walker

Refrain

Je - sus, you are bread for us. Je - sus, you are life for us.
In your gift of Eu - cha - rist we find love. love, we find love.

Verses

1. When we feel we need a friend
2. When we feel that we need love
3. When we feel that things aren't fair
4. In com - mu - nion we be - lieve
5. Gath - ered in God's fam - i - ly
6. When we help our fam - i - lies
7. When we help the hun - gry ones
8. When we help the thirst - y ones

1-8. you are there with us, Je - sus. Thank you for the
1-8. friend you are. Thank you for the love we share.

Eucharist

229

We Come Today

Mark Friedman

Refrain

We come to-day to break this bread and share this cup of wine. We gath-er at your ta-ble now to hear your words of life. And though there are so man-y here to-day, we all are one: one fam-i-ly, one bod-y, and one Church;

1-4 we are your own. *(to Verses)* *Final* we are your own.

Verses

1. We thank you, God, for Je - sus, who calls us to this feast
2. We thank you for our par - ents who care for us each day,
3. We thank you for the peo - ple who teach us in your ways,
4. We thank you for cre - a - tion, the beau-ty of the earth;

to Refrain

1. to share in one com - mu - nion in your name.
2. the fam - 'ly gath - ered 'round us here in love.
3. who help us learn to love our neigh-bors well.
4. with grate-ful hearts we thank you for your gifts.

Come, Holy Spirit

Tom Booth

Refrain

Come, Ho - ly Spir - it; come with your pow'r.

Rous-ing your peo - ple, come in this hour.

Verse 1

1. There's a gaze of love, an in - ti-mate look of ac-

1. cept-ance and joy. There's a smile and laugh, an

to Refrain

1. e - ter - nal dance be-tween Fa - ther and Son.

Verse 2

2. You are per - fect love giv - en a - bove from the lov -

2. - er. Cast-ing out all our fear, let us

to Refrain

2. live in joy, let us live with-in the be-loved.

Verse 3

3. With the bold - ness of saints and a - ban - don that ech -

3. - oes the proph - ets; like the wit-ness of those who

to Refrain

3. gave of their lives nev-er a-shamed of the cross.

Confirmation

231

Envía Tu Espíritu

Bob Hurd

Refrain

En - ví-a tu Es-pí-ri-tu, en - ví-a tu Es-pí-ri-tu,

en - ví-a tu Es-pí-ri-tu, se-a re-no-va-da

la faz de la tie - rra. Se-a re-no-

va - da la faz de la tie - rra.

Verses

1. Ven, es-pí - ri - tu de a - mor, man -
   _ *Spir - it of the liv - ing God,* *burn*
2. Dul - ce bri - sa, san - to don y
   _ *Wind of prom - ise, wind of change,* *friend*
3. Por tu gra - cia y tu bon - dad, ven,
   _ *Breath of life and ho - li - ness,* *heal*

1. da tu luz y haz - nos un pue -
   _ *in our hearts,* *and make us a peo -*
2. pro - tec - tor, re - nue - va la tie -
   _ *of the poor,* *em - pow - er your peo -*
3. sá - na - nos, que no ha - ya pe - ca -
   ev - 'ry wound, *and lead us be - yond*

to Refrain

1. - blo de fe y es - pe - ran - za.
   _ *- ple of hope and com - pas - sion.*
2. - rra con paz y jus - ti - cia.
   _ *- ple to make peace and jus - tice.*
3. - do en el al - ma del pue - blo.
   ev - 'ry sin that di - vides us.

Text: Based on Psalm 104:30 and the Pentecost Sequence; refrain and English verses adapt. by Bob Hurd; Spanish verses adapt. by Jaime Cortez.
Text and music © 1988, 2000, Bob Hurd. Published by OCP. All rights reserved.

Confirmation

God Is Calling Your Name

Mark Friedman and Janet Vogt

Refrain: All

God is call - ing your name. Be - fore you were born, God reached out and held your life in his hands.

to Verses

Final

sing 3 times

God is call - ing your name.

Verses: Cantor

1. Like the Spir - it com - ing down on the wings of a
2. Like the lil - ies of the field as they flow - er and
3. Like the sun - light on your face as each new day be -

1. dove, God will brush a - gainst you and a - noint
2. bloom, like the lit - tle spar - row, God is al -
3. gins, like the dance of ev - 'ry breeze, God whis -

3 **to Refrain**

1. you with his ho - ly love.
2. - ways watch - ing o - ver you.
3. - pers to you on the wind.

Confirmation

233

Holy Spirit

Ken Canedo

Ostinato Refrain: All

Ho - ly Spir - it, come in - to our lives.

Ho - ly Spir - it, make us tru - ly wise.

Verses
Cantor

1. Give us a spir - it of wis - dom, an un - der - stand -
2. Give us a spir - it of cour - age, and judg - ment that
3. Spir - it of love and com - pas - sion, give hope to all
4. Spir - it of all con - so - la - tion, O lift our hearts
5. Spir - it of light and of wis - dom, O lift us from
6. Spir - it of strength and of heal - ing, bend stub - born heart

All

Ho - ly Spir - it, come in - to

1. - ing heart. _____ Give us a spir - it of knowl -
2. is wise. _____ Give us a spir - it of rev -
3. the poor. _____ Spir - it of jus - tice and mer -
4. this day. _____ Spir - it of all un - der - stand -
5. our sor - row. _ Spir - it of peace and for - give -
6. and will. _____ Spir - it of trust and of car -

our lives. Ho - ly

to Refrain

1. - edge, and lead us to the truth. _____
2. - 'rence, of won - der and of awe. _____
3. - cy, come o - pen ev - 'ry door. _____
4. - ing, O help us know your way. _____
5. - ness, O help us face to - mor - row. _
6. - ing, O melt us, warm our chill. _____

to Refrain

Spir - it, make us tru - ly wise.

Text: Verses 1 & 2 based on Isaiah 11:2; verses 3–6 based on the Pentecost Sequence. Text and music © 1998, Ken Canedo.
Published by spiritandsong.com®, a division of OCP. All rights reserved.

Confirmation

Put On Christ

234

Bob Hurd

Verses 1, 2: Cantor (or All)

1. We have come to this feast, called by love
2. We be-come what we share: Bread of Life,

1. for love, keep-ing mem-'ry of the Lord.
2. Je-sus, blessed and bro-ken for the world.

Refrain: All

Put on Christ. Put on Christ. Come to the wa-ters of ev-er-last-ing life. Put on Christ. Put on Christ. Walk in the free-dom of the chil-dren.

| 1 to Verse 2 | 2 to Verse 3 | Final |

of God. God. God.

Verse 3: Cantor (or All)

3. We have seen God's sav - ing love in an earth - ly
3. time and place: God's own glo - ry in a
3. hu - man face.

to Refrain

Confirmation

235　You Have Called Us

Bernadette Farrell

Refrain: 1st time: Cantor, All repeat; thereafter: All

You have called us by our name. We be-long to you.
You have called us by our name and we are yours.

Verses

1. You have cho-sen us to be mem-bers
2. You will lead us to your light, walk be-
3. You will hold us when we fall, give new
4. You will nour-ish, you will lead, giv-ing
5. Through our shar-ing here to-day may our

1. of your fam-i-ly. In your love you have cre-
2. fore us through the night. You will guide us on our
3. strength to hear your call. You will nev-er be be-
4. ev-'ry gift we need, for your reign will be es-
5. faith and life con-vey Christ our light and Christ our

to Refrain

1. at-ed us to live in u-ni-ty.
2. jour-ney. You will keep our vi-sion bright.
3. yond us, for your love is all in all.
4. tab-lished from the small-est of all seeds.
5. vi-sion, Christ our pur-pose, Christ our way.

Confirmation

Verses, ST. THOMAS, Tantum Ergo,
John F. Wade (1711–1786)
Refrain by Matt Maher

Verses

1. Down in ad-o-ra-tion fall-ing, this great sac-ra-ment we hail;
2. To the ev-er-last-ing Fa-ther, and the Son who reigns on high,
3. Pour up-on us, Lord of mer-cy, spir-it of thy self-less love.

1. o-ver an-cient forms de-part-ing new-er rites of grace pre-vail;
2. with the Spir-it blest, pro-ceed-ing forth from each e-ter-nal-ly,
3. Make of us one true heart yearn-ing for the glo-ry of thy Son,

1. faith for all de-fects sup-ply-ing where the fee-ble
2. be sal-va-tion, hon-or, bless-ing, might and end-less
3. Je-sus, fire of jus-tice blaz-ing, gladd-'ning light for-

to Verse 2 *2, 3*

1. sens-es fail.
2. maj-es-ty.
3. ev-er-more.

Refrain

Je-sus, Lamb of God, sav-ing love for all, Lord of heav'n and

earth, Fa-ther's love for all; I bow to you. Je-sus, Lamb of

God, sav-ing love for all, Lord of heav'n and earth; I bow to

Interlude **11** *to Verse 3*

you, bow to you, I bow to you.

Final

you, bow to you, bow to you, I bow to you.

King of My Heart

Greg Walton

Verses

1. Fill me, I'm an emp - ty ves-sel; make me whole,
2. Bread of life,___ blessed and bro-ken; make us whole,
3. Sa - cred cup of our sal - va-tion; make us whole,

1. king of my heart, king of my heart.
2, 3. king of our hearts, king of our hearts.

1. Fill me, I'm an emp - ty ves-sel; make me whole,
2. Bread of life,___ blessed and bro-ken; make us whole,
3. Sa - cred cup of our sal - va-tion; make us whole,

1. king of my heart, king of my heart.
2, 3. king of our hearts, king of our hearts.

Refrain

You are Lord, Lord.

You are Lord and king { of my heart.
{ of our hearts.
{ of our hearts.

Exposition/Adoration

We Fall Down

Chris Tomlin

We fall down, we lay our crowns at the feet of Je-

-sus, the great-ness of mer-cy and love, at the feet

of Je - sus. And we cry, "Ho - ly, ho - ly, ho-

- ly." And we cry, "Ho - ly, ho - ly, ho - ly." And we cry,

"Ho - ly, ho - ly, ho - ly is the Lamb."

Ho - ly, ho - ly, ho - ly is the Lamb.

Exposition/Adoration

239 Behold the Lamb of God

Matt Maher

Verse

ɤ You are my Lord.___ It's you I a - dore.___
Your might hum-bles ev - 'ry___ heart;___ the high - est of heav -

- ens___ bow.___ Noth-ing on earth could ev - er take

[1] [2] your place. And now we see your

sac - ri - fice, the great - est gift, our great - est prize. Be -

Refrain

hold the Lamb of God! Be - hold the Lamb of God who

[1] [3] to Verse [2] to Bridge

takes a - way the sins of the world. world.

Final (Coda)

world. Be - hold the Lamb of God!

Who takes a - way the sins of the world, the sins of

the world, the sins of the world.

Bridge

We will not for-get, we will stay a-wake!

We will not a-ban - don the

pro-mise that you made. We will not for-get, Be -

1

2 to Refrain and Final ending

240 You Alone

Sarah Hart and Dwight Liles

Refrain

You a-lone are ho-ly, you a-lone are Lord.
You a-lone are wor-thy to be hon-ored and a-dored.
Mer-cy you have giv-en, kind-ness you have shown.
Love is you a-lone.

1. to Verse 1

2. 7 to Verse 2 | Final

Love is you a-lone.

Verses

1. Who of us is sin-less in this place?
2. What is there to do but thank you, then,

1. Who of us de-serves your sav-ing grace?
2. for the gift that we might call you friend?

1. Who of us is good at all with-out your bless-
2. Great-er love has not been known than that for which

1. -ed love that falls up-on our hearts to
2. you gave your on-ly son, that you might

2 to Refrain

1. heal our bro-ken-ness?
2. see us, pure and blessed.

Exposition/Adoration

Come to the River

241

Bob Hurd

Refrain

Come, O come, come to the riv - er
flow - ing from the bod - y of Christ.
We'll go down, deep in the wa - ter,
but in the Lord we shall a - rise.

Verses

1. Washed in wa - ters of re-birth,
2. Priest - ly peo - ple are ___ we,
3. Blest are those ___ who ___ thirst
4. Let us walk ___ in the light
5. Those who sow ___ in ___ tears

to Refrain

1. we have put on Christ Je - sus.
2. sealed and sent by the Spir - it.
3. for the reign of God's jus - tice.
4. of God's ho - ly prom - ise.
5. reap the har - vest re - joic - ing.

*Repeat phrase final time.

Catechesis

242 Don't Rock the Boat

Mark Friedman

Verses

1. ⁀ Je - sus___ got in a fish - ing boat.
2. They did - n't___ have a chart or map.
3. The waves___ grew high, they tossed the boat.
4. He raised his___ hand up to the sky.
5. "We're sor - ry,___ Lord," said Pe - ter then.
6. When fear has___ got a - hold of you.

Don't

1-6. rock the boat, have faith!

At least that's what Saint
And Je - sus was a -
"We're gon - na drown,___ can't
And to the waves, "Be
"It's just we're weak and
Re - mem-ber that___ your

1. Mat-thew wrote.
2. sleep in back.
3. stay a - float!"
4. still," he cried.
5. sin - ful men."
6. God is true.

Don't rock the boat, have faith!

1. His friends, they crowd - ed in with him, and
2. A long day's preach - ing o - ver and the
3. ⁀ "Je - sus, save us!" Pe - ter cried, "Wake
4. And sud - den - ly the sea be - came at
5. Then Je - sus smiled and said that he'd stay
6. Like Pe - ter, we all fail at times, but

1. off they sailed with hope.
2. sky had just turned black.
3. up, we have no hope."
4. peace be - fore their eyes.
5. with them 'til the end.
6. God will see us through.

Catechesis

Refrain

Have faith! Don't rock the boat. Don't rock the boat, have faith! Have faith! You'll stay a - float, you'll stay a - float, have faith!

1-5, to Verses

Final

faith!

Have faith! Don't rock the boat. Don't rock the boat, have faith!

Sacred Silence   243

Tom Booth and Jenny Pixler

Refrain
Sa - cred si - lence, ho - ly o - cean, gen - tle wa - ter,

Verses
1. God my Fa - ther, Christ my broth - er, Ho - ly Spir - it,
2. Ho - ly Ma - ry, gen - tle moth - er, God's pure ves - sel,

wash - ing o - ver me; help me lis - ten, Ho - ly
1. sanc - ti - fy - ing me; Lord, I'm sor - ry, please for -
2. pray - ing for me; saints and an - gels, all in

Spir - it. Come and speak to me. (to Verses)
1. give me. Come and set me free. (to Refrain)
2. heav - en, come and be with me. (to Refrain)

Final

Come and be with me. Come and speak to me.

Catechesis

244 Do the Right Thing

Bob Halligan Jr.

Catechesis

Jonah, What Will You Do

Janet Vogt

245

Refrain

Jo-nah, Jo-nah, what will you do? Lis-ten, God is call-
ing to you! Oh, Jo-nah, what will you do
when our God is call-ing to you?

Verses

1. Tides roll in, tides roll out.
2. Waves roll on, waves roll high.
3. The might-y seas, they toss and turn.
4. Land ho! Here we go!

1. Faith has a way of still-ing those lit-tle voic-
2. Just when you least ex-pect it, a storm comes rush-
3. God has a way of teach-ing you things that you
4. Just look a-round, you've found your feet on sol-

1. -es of doubt. O-ceans deep,
2. -ing by. Wind and rain,
3. must learn. So when you set your
4. -id ground. God is good,

1. o-ceans wide; God has a way
2. sleet and hail; just when you least
3. course to sail, point your-self toward God
4. God is true. Out of the depths of dark-

to Refrain

1. of find-ing you when you want to hide!
2. ex-pect it, you run in-to a whale!
3. and you will nev-er run in-to a whale!
4. -ness, God de-liv-ers me and you!

Catechesis

246 I Will Have Faith in You

Sarah Hart and Sam Mizell

Verses

1. When the night is clos - ing in, I will have
2. If my feet should lose their way, I will have
3. (Instrumental)

1. faith in you. When I've lost all hope
2. faith in you, to bring me to a rest -

1. with - in, I will have faith in you.
2. - ing place.

Refrain

Faith is be - liev - ing in all that love can do,

and I am in your keep - ing, so I will have faith in you. *to Coda*

1. | 2. to Verse 2 | 2. to Bridge

Bridge

I will be hope - ful. I will not lose heart. I will

be trust-ing in ev-'ry-thing you are. *to Verse 3*

Coda

Faith is be-liev - ing in all that love can do, and I am in your keep-ing so I will have faith in you. I will have faith in you. I will have faith in you.

Catechesis

247   I Am Your Friend

Paule Freeburg, DC and Christopher Walker

Refrain

I am your friend, al-ways here be-side you,
to watch and be with you in all that you do.
I am your friend, I am your friend.

Verses

1. We will fol-low Je-sus' way, to his cross, with him we
2. Je-sus helps us ev-'ry day in the fears that come our
3. Je-sus helps us ev-'ry day in our work and in our
4. Je-sus guides us ev-'ry day, al-ways show-ing us the
5. In his love and care we stay, as we hear his call to-
6. Je-sus prom-ised he would stay in the bread and wine each
7. As a fam-i-ly we pray to be close to him each

to Refrain

1. stay, in our hearts to him we say:
2. way, in our hearts we hear him say:
3. play, in our hearts we hear him say:
4. way, in our hearts we hear him say:
5. day: in our hearts we hear him say:
6. day: in our hearts we hear him say:
7. day, in our hearts we hear him say:

Catechesis

Jacob's Ladder

248

Mark Friedman and Janet Vogt

1. Lost on the road, Ja - cob, so far from home,
2. You are the one, Ja - cob, cho - sen by God,
3. Ev - en like you, Ja - cob, when we're con-fused,

1. run-ning a - way from your God.
2. walk-ing a path few have gone.
3. we turn our face from our God.

1. Though you are scared, Ja - cob, hold to your dreams.
2. Like A - bra - ham, Ja - cob, look to the stars.
3. But just like you, Ja - cob, we can walk on.

Refrain

For if you climb the lad - der, Ja - cob's lad - der, climb

up to the sky, for the dream you dream is true,

1, 2

God will al - ways be with you if you climb.

to Verses 2, 3 | *3 to Refrain* | *Final*

if you climb,

if you climb.

Catechesis

249   Jump in the Water

Sarah Hart

Verses

1. Mo - ses and his peo - ple run - ning from the Pha-
2. Je - sus - 's dis - ci - ples, sail - ing on the o -

1. - raoh past the cit - y gates out to the
2. - cean, black clouds spin - ning 'round them in the

1. big wide sea. As they reached the wa - ter,
2. storm - y sea, Je - sus called out to them,

1. had no - where else to go, God told Mo - ses "Keep
2. walked right on that wa - ter, told them, "Get out of

1. on mov - ing, trust in me." God said:
2. the boat, come walk with me." God said:

Refrain   (Shout)

Jump, *(Jump!)* jump in the wa - ter. Jump, *(Jump!)* jump

in the wa - ter. Jump, *(Jump!)* jump in the wa - ter.

1

Do not be a - fraid. God said:
(Last time) God says:

2   2nd time: to Bridge   Interlude   **8** 1st time: to Verse 2

Do not be a - fraid.

Catechesis

Do not be a-fraid. Do not be a-fraid.

Bridge

All this world is like an o-cean, so un-known, so deep and wide. We may feel a-fraid, un-sure, but God is al-ways stand-ing in the mid-dle of the tide, say-ing,

Terra, Terra Sancta

250

Jack Miffleton

Refrain

The earth is a-live with the glo-ry of God.

Round

Ter-ra, ter-ra san-cta; this is ho-ly ground, ho-ly, ho-ly ground. ho-ly ground.

Catechesis

251 Overflow

Matt Maher

Verses

1. Your grace is pow-er,___ your will
2. Your word: true pres-ence.___ Your bod-y:
3. Your wor-ship of you,___ it's your gift

1. for-ev-er,___ your love is a riv-er;
2. our rec-om-pense. Your blood: sal-va-tion;
3. to us from_ you. No one could give this gift but you;

1 to Verse 2 | 2, 3

1-3. o-ver-flow in me. 2, 3.

Refrain

O-ver-flow in me, my Lord, o-ver-flow in me, my Lord.

Let your peo-ple bless you as your cup is poured; o-ver-

to Coda | 1 to Verse 3 | 3

flow in me, my Lord, o-ver-flow in me, my Lord.

2 to Bridge | 3 to Refrain and Coda

Lord, o-ver-flow in me, my Lord. Lord.

Bridge

We lift up our hearts. We lift up our souls. We lift up our minds. Ev'ry good thing is yours. Yeah, ev-'ry good thing is yours, so o-ver-flow.

6

to Refrain

Oh,

Coda

Lord, o-ver-flow in me, my Lord. O-ver-flow in me, my Lord. O-ver-flow. Oh. O-ver-flow in me, my Lord. O-ver-flow in me, my Lord. O-ver-flow in me, my Lord.

Catechesis

252

Golden

Christopher M. Padgett

Catechesis

Shepherd Song

Janet Vogt

Refrain: 1st time: Cantor, All repeat; thereafter: All

Shep - herd in the fields of green, Shep - herd on the moun - tain - side, al - ways ev - er be my guide.

1-4 1: to Refrain
2-4: to Verses

Final

I will fol - low you.

I will fol - low you.

Verses
Cantor

1. Where I turn, there you are. If I'm lost, you're not far.
2. If I stray you ap - pear, call - ing me to come near.
3. Shel - ter me from the storm. Keep me safe from all harm.

All

to Refrain

1. Lead - ing me lov - ing - ly;
2. You for - give all I do;   } I will fol - low you.
3. Where you go I'll go, too;

Catechesis

254

Here Am I, Lord

Curtis Stephan

Refrain

Here am I, Lord; I come to do your will.

Here am I, Lord. Here am I.

[1, 5]

[2-4 to Verses] [Final]

Here am I. Here am I.

Verse 1

1. I wait - ed for you and you heard me, O God.

1. You have put a new song in - to my mouth:

1. a hymn of praise to the God, to the

to Refrain

1. God of my sal - va - tion.

Verse 2

2. You o - pened my ear to your word, O God.

2. You take no de - light in emp - ty sac - ri - fice.

2. To do your will is my life, my

to Refrain

2. life and my de - light, O Lord.

Verse 3

3. I sing of your jus - tice; I sing of your peace.

3. I sing your praise in the midst, in the

2   to Refrain

3. midst of all your peo - ple.

255 On a Mission/En Mission/Y Me Da una Misión

Julie Lafontaine and Bernie Cossentino

Refrain

English: I am called, I am called, I am called
French: Vo - ca - tion, Vo - ca - tion, Une mis - sion
Spanish: Me lla - ma, me lla - ma y me da u-

on a mis-sion to love and serve the Lord.
nous at - tend___ et je veux ê - tre là.
- na mi - sión,___ ser - vir___ al Se - ñor. Me

I am called, I am called,
Me voi - ci, j'ai une vo - ca - tion,
lla - ma, me lla - ma

to Verses/Bridge

I am called on a mis - sion.___
Dieu m'en - voie en mis - sion.___
Me in - vi - ta a su mi - sión.___

Final

We are called on a mis - sion.___ Yes,
Dieu m'en - voie en mis-sion.___
Me in - vi - ta a su mi - sión.___ Sí,

we are called on a mis - sion.
Dieu m'en - voie en mis-sion.___
me in - vi - ta a su mi - sión.___

English
1. Jesus is my teacher, the mentor of my life;
   he calls me to the altar, the gentle sacrifice.
   He beckons me, I answer, though at times I run and hide,
   but hearing him, my heart is opened wide.

2. Jesus is my shepherd, he leads me on my way,
   and I in turn must lead those who may have gone astray.
   I feel his call to follow and he wants me to explore,
   and follow in his footsteps and love him evermore.

Bridge
   He sends us on a mission we may not understand;
   if we had his vision, we'd all rise to take a stand.
   When I put my trust in him, he cradles me with love,
   bringing me his peace from up above.

3. Jesus is my savior, he gives me everyday
   the gift of my vocation I'll never throw away.
   So here I stand before him and offer him my vow;
   he's called me on a mission to reach out, reach out.

Français
1. Jésus, tu es mon guide, Le maître de ma vie
   Tu m'invites à ta table, À ton Eucharistie.
   Je réponds à ton appel, Même si parfois je suis lent
   J'entends ta voix et mon coeur s'ouvre grand.

2. Jésus, Ô bon Berger, c'est toi qui me conduis
   Et à mon tour je guide, Tous ceux qui ont fui.
   Je veux toujours te suivre, Et marcher dans tes pas
   Au long de mon chemin, Je sais que tu es là.

Bridge
   Partager son rêve, en mission il nous attend.
   Bâtir son Royaume, Tous ensemble, toi et moi.
   Je mets ma foi en lui, Son amour me façonne
   Sa joie, sa paix, chaque jour il me les donne.

3. Jésus, Sauveur, tu donnes, Les plus précieux des dons
   Pour nous et pour ton peuple, La vie, la vocation
   Nos voeux et nos promesses, Nos vies, nous les offrons
   Avec toi et pour toi en mission, mission.

Español
1. Jesús, maestro, compañero de mi vida,
   me llamas al altar, al tierno Sacrificio.
   Me invitas, y digo, "Sí", pero a veces esquivo.
   Al escucharte mi corazón se abre.

2. Jesús mi pastor, me conduces por tus sendas.
   También voy a guiar a los desviados.
   Siento tu llamado, quieres que te siga,
   que camine en tus pasos, que te ame más y más.

Bridge
   Compartes tu sueño; no comprendemos.
   Si tuviéramos tu visión, no dudaríamos.
   Cuando confío en ti, me acoges en tu amor
   Tu paz y tu alegría recibo día a día.

3. Jesús mi Salvador, cada día me regalas,
   mi vocación, precioso don, que nunca olvidaré.
   Aquí estoy ante ti, te ofrezco mi promesa.
   Me has llamado para amar, para que te siga, te siga.

256

The Call

Tom Franzak

Verse 1

1. Fa-ther, you knew me be-fore my moth-er's womb,

1. but what you're ask - ing seems way too much too soon.

1. I'm not a teach-er or a speak-er; I'm much too

young and full of fear. But still you say you'll

speak through me in spite of my young years.

Refrain

Wher-ev-er you send me, I will go. Send me,

Lord, send me, Lord. What-ev-er you tell me,

I will speak. Send me, Lord, send me,

1 Lord.

2 to Verse 2

Final

Lord. Send me, Lord, send me,

Lord.

Vocations

2. Cleanse my heart and soul, wash a - way my fear.

2. Place your words in my mouth and de - liv - er me,

2.   de - liv - er me.

2 to Refrain

257 Be the Hands, the Heart of God

Janet Vogt and Mark Friedman

Refrain: 1st time: Cantor, All repeat; thereafter: All

Be the hands, the heart of God. Go in - to the world and share God's spir - it. Spread the mes - sage, be the song. Save a lit - tle bit, then pass it on.

(1st time: Repeat) to Verses | 6 to Refrain | Final

it on. it on.

Save a lit - tle bit, then pass it on.

Verses
Cantor / All

1-4. Sons and daugh - ters,
1. peace be - fore you,
2. love be - fore you,
3. light be - fore you,
4. Christ be - fore you,

Cantor / All

1-4. sis - ters, broth - ers,
1. peace be - hind you.
2. love be - hind you.
3. light be - hind you.
4. Christ be - hind you.

Cantor

1. Peace sur - round you, one and all.
2. Love sur - round you, one and all.
3. Light sur - round you, one and all.
4. Christ sur - round you, one and all.

All to Refrain

1-4. Save a lit - tle bit, then pass it on.

Service/Outreach

Give Me Ears to Listen

Timothy R. Smith

Verses

1, 4. Let me be your ser-vant; let me walk your way.
2. In si - lence, when you call me, let me hear your voice.
3. Last night, when I a-woke I heard you call my name.

1, 4. Guide me on your path; give night the light of day. When
2. Je - sus, walk be - side me; let my soul re - joice. When
3. You re-freshed my soul; I felt your burn - ing flame. Oh,

1, 4. Let me be a sure foun - da - tion, pure and strong.
2. winds and cur - rents bat - ter me, help me be sure.
3. strength - en me to bear my cross and walk your way.

1, 4. Let me tell of your sal - va - tion all life long.
2. Give me cour - age from the storms when they oc - cur.
3. Give me grace to com - fort those with all I say.

Refrain

Give me ears to lis - ten. Give me eyes to see. Give me words to

1, 3, Final
to Vss. 2, 4
(Fine)

2
to Verse 3

speak and show your face to me. me.

259 Go Light Your World

Chris Rice

Verses 1, 2

1. There is a can - dle in ev - 'ry
2. Frus - trat - ed broth - er, see how he's

1. soul; _____ some bright - ly burn - ing, some dark and
2. tried to light his own can - dle some oth - er

1. cold. There is a Spir - it who brings a
2. way. See now your sis - ter, she's been robbed and

1. fire, _____ ig - nites a can - dle and makes his home.
2. lied _ to, still holds a can - dle with - out a flame.

Refrain

So, car - ry your can - dle, run to the dark - ness, seek out the

1. hope - less, con - fused and torn.
2. lone - ly, the tired and worn.

Hold out your can - dle

for all to see it. Take your can - dle and go light your

|1

world. Take your can - dle and go light your world.

to Verse 2 |2   to Verse 3

can - dle and go light your world.

Verse 3

3. We are a fam - 'ly whose hearts are blaz - ing,

3. so let's raise our can - dles and light up the sky,

3. pray - ing to our Fa - ther, in the name of Je - sus:

3. make us a bea - con in dark-est time. So, car - ry your

Final Refrain

can - dle, run to the dark - ness, seek out the

{ help - less, de - ceived and poor. }
{ hope - less, con - fused and torn. } Hold out your

can - dle for all to see it. Take your

1

can - dle and go light your world. Car - ry your

Final

can - dle and go light your world. Take your

can - dle and go light your world.

260   Go Make a Difference

Steve Angrisano and Tom Tomaszek

Refrain

Go make a dif - f'rence. We can make a dif- -f'rence. Go make a dif - f'rence in the world.

Go make a dif - f'rence. We can make a dif- -f'rence. Go make a dif - f'rence in the world.

to Verses
last time: to Coda ⊕

Verses 1, 2

1. We are the salt of the earth, called to let the peo - ple
2. We are the hands of __ Christ reach-ing out to those in

1. see the love of God in you and me.
2. need, the face of God for all to see.

1. We are the light of the world, __ not to be hid - den but be
2. We are the spir - it of hope; _____ ⅔ we are the voice of

to Refrain

1. seen. Go make a dif - f'rence in the world.
2. peace. Go make a dif - f'rence in the world.

Verse 3

3. So let your love shine on, let it shine for all to

3. see. Go make a dif - f'rence in the world.

3. And the spir - it of Christ will be with us as we

to Refrain

3. go. Go make a dif - f'rence in the world.

⊕ Coda

Go make a dif - f'rence in the world.

Go make a dif - f'rence in the world.

Text: Based on Matthew 5:13–16. Text and music © 1997, Steve Angrisano and Thomas N. Tomaszek.
Published by spiritandsong.com®, a division of OCP. All rights reserved.

261   I Will Choose Christ

Tom Booth

Refrain

I will choose Christ, I will choose love, I choose to serve.

I give my heart, I give my life, I give my all

1-4   to Verses
last time: to Refrain   *Final*

to you.   to you.   I give my all to you.

Verse 1

1. How man-y times must he call my name and show to

1. me that he is God? And as a ser-vant he

to Refrain

1. calls to me, "You must serve too."

Verse 2

2. Christ, my teach-er and heal-er, teach my

2. heart and heal my soul. And as I walk this

to Refrain

2. road with you, teach me to love.

Verse 3

3. As I look up-on your cross, so too

3. must I die with you. And with the death of my

to Refrain

3. own de - sires, I'll rise with you.

262

I Will Testify

Curtis Stephan, Jesse Manibusan
and Sarah Hart

Refrain

I will tes-ti-fy and glo-ri-fy the name of Je - sus. I will not de-ny, I will re-ly on Je - sus. - sus. *I will stand*

1-3, Final (Fine) / *to Verses* / *4 to Bridge Soloist*

Verses

1. When waves of fear come crash-in' in
2. When con-fu-sion set-tles in
3. In this Pas-chal mys-ter-y,

1. and all my friends all walk a-way,
2. and all this pres-sure's got me down,
3. in your lov-ing sac-ri-fice,

1. stand-in' firm-ly on your word you see me
2. I won't be fol-low-in' the crowd. So give me
3. as I fol-low in your ways, I wan-na

to Refrain

1. through the pain, you give me strength a-gain.
2. strength, O Lord, to live my faith out loud.
3. be like you and give my life a-way.

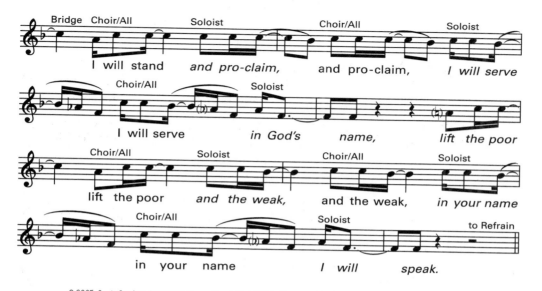

Bridge

I will stand *and pro-claim,* and pro-claim, *I will serve*

I will serve *in God's name,* lift the poor

lift the poor *and the weak,* and the weak, *in your name*

in your name *I will speak.*

Light of the World

Gerard Chiusano

Refrain

I am the light, the light of the world. Who - ev - er

fol - lows me will have the light of life. I am the

light, the light of the world. Who - ev - er

fol - lows me will have the light of life.

Verse 1

1. Take up your cross and be my dis - ci - ple.

to Refrain

1. De - ny your - self and come fol - low me.

Verse 2

2. Who - ev - er be - lieves in me be - lieves in him who sent me.

to Refrain

2. And who - ev - er sees me sees him who sent me.

Verse 3

3. I have come as light to the world

to Refrain

3. so that all who be - lieve will not be in dark - ness.

4. I come not to judge the world but to save all peo-ple.

4. I come to bring all peo-ple to the Fa-ther.

to Refrain

Based on John 8:12; 12:44–47. Text and music © 1998, Gerard Chiusano. Published by OCP. All rights reserved.

Here I Am, Lord

264

Dan Schutte

Verses

1. I, the Lord of sea and sky, I have heard my peo-ple cry.
2. I, the Lord of snow and rain, I have borne my peo-ple's pain.
3. I, the Lord of wind and flame, I will tend the poor and lame.

1. All who dwell in dark and sin My hand will save. I, who
2. I have wept for love of them. They turn a - way. I will
3. I will set a feast for them. My hand will save. Fin-est

1. made the stars of night, I will make their dark-ness bright.
2. break their hearts of stone, Give them hearts for love a - lone.
3. bread I will pro - vide Till their hearts be sat - is - fied.

1. Who will bear my light to them? Whom shall I send?
2. I will speak my word to them. Whom shall I send?
3. I will give my life to them. Whom shall I send?

Refrain

Here I am, Lord. Is it I, Lord? I have heard you

call-ing in the night. I will go, Lord, if you

lead me. I will hold your peo-ple in my heart.

Text: Based on Isaiah 6. Text and music © 1981, OCP. All rights reserved.

Witnesses

Paul Hillebrand

Refrain: All

We will be your wit-ness-es to all the world.

We will be your wit-ness-es to all the world. *Fine*

Verses
Cantor

1. Make dis - ci - ples, ___ make dis - ci - ples ___ of
2. Spread the news, ___ spread the news ___ a -
3. Thank the Lord, ___ thank the Lord ___ for

All

1. ev - 'ry-one _ we meet, of ev - 'ry-one _ we meet.
2. cross ___ the land, a - cross ___ the land.
3. gath - er-ing _ us here, for gath - er-ing _ us here.

Cantor   All   Cantor

1. You have called, you have called ___ us to be,
2. You have come, you have come _ to give to us, to
3. We will be, we will be ___ your wit - ness - es, your

All   Cantor   All   Cantor/All   to Refrain

1. us to be ___ light to all, ___ light to all ___ the world. ___
2. give to us ___ peace of mind, _ peace of mind _ for - ev - er.
3. wit - ness - es _ to all, ___ to all ___ the world. ___

Service/Outreach

Hey, You, Stand Up for God

266

Livia and ValLimar Jansen

1. Hey, you, stand up for God. Hey, you, stand up for God.
2. Hey, you, just trust in God. Hey, you, just trust in God.
3. Hey, you, show love for God. Hey, you, show love for God.
4. Hey, you, now clap for God. Hey, you, now clap for God.
5. Hey, you, stand up for God. Hey, you, stand up for God.

1. Hey, you, stand up for God, 'cause God stands up for you.
2. Hey, you, just trust in God, 'cause our God trusts in you.
3. Hey, you, show love for God, 'cause God shows love for you.
4. Hey, you, now clap for God, 'cause our God claps for you.
5. Hey, you, stand up for God, 'cause God stands up for you.

6. Hey, you, stand up for God. Stand up for God.

6. Hey, you, stand up for God. Stand up for God!

Discipleship

267

Do Not Fear

Cyprian Consiglio

Refrain

Do not fear, my lit-tle flock, for the Fa-ther is glad to give you the king-dom.

Wher-ev-er your trea-sure is, there al-so your heart will be, and the Fa-ther is glad to be your shield.

Final: shield, and the Fa-ther is glad to be your shield.

Verse 1
1. I have come not for the rich; I have come for the poor of soul. I have come not for the strong; I have come for the weak of heart.

Verse 2
2. Look at the birds of the air! Learn from the flow-ers of the field! If the Lord can ar-ray them in such splen-dor, how much more must he care for you?

Discipleship

Verse 3

3. I give you my word, you who've giv-en up
3. homes, you who've giv-en up wealth for the sake of the
3. king-dom; you will re-ceive a thou-sand times
3. more in this pres-ent age and e-ter-nal life.

to Refrain

Discipleship

268

My Sheep

Tom Booth

Refrain

My sheep hear my voice and they all fol - low me.

Verse 1

1. Sing to the Lord with joy all you lands.

1. Serve the Lord with glad - ness.

to Refrain

1. Come be-fore him with joy - ful song.

Verse 2

2. Know that the Lord is God, he is King.

2. He made us; his we are;

to Refrain

2. his peo-ple, the flock he tends.

Text: Based on John 10:27; Psalm 100:1–2, 3. Text and music © 1993, Tom Booth. Published by spiritandsong.com®, a division of OCP. All rights reserved.

We Belong to You

Trevor Thomson

Refrain

We be-long to you, O Lord of our long-ing, We be-long to you. In our dai-ly liv-ing, dy-ing and ris-ing We be-long to you. *(to Verses)* | *Last time* We be-long to you. We be-long to you.

Verses

1. In the wa-ters of your mer-cy, When the
2. Filled with gifts and filled with good-ness, Spir-it
3. When we share the bread you've bro-ken With the
4. We are called to share your word, Lord, In all we

1. old be-comes the new, Souls u-nit-ed in the
2. breath-ing life in-to All who seek to find their
3. man-y and the few, We are blessed and we are
4. say and all we do. As our jour-ney moves us

to Refrain

1. mys-t'ry:
2. pur-pose:
3. bro-ken;
4. on-ward,
We be-long to you.

Discipleship

270 Never Too Young

Carey Landry

Verses

1. Nev-er too young to preach the Gos - pel; nev-er too young to
2. Nev-er too young to feed the hun - gry; nev-er too young to
3. Nev-er too young to sing to-geth - er; nev-er too young to

1. bring Good News! Nev-er too young to work for jus - tice;
2. help the poor. Nev-er too young to care for oth - ers;
3. pray as one. Nev-er too young to praise and wor - ship;

1. nev-er too young to be God's Light!
2. nev-er too young to be God's Love! We are
3. nev-er too young to be God's Song!

Refrain
Choir/All

nev-er too young to wit - ness, we are nev-er too young to serve;

we are nev-er too young to be dis - ci - ples of our Lord!

We are nev-er too young to wit - ness, we are

nev-er too young to serve; we are nev-er too young to be

1, 2: to Verses 2, 3
3: to Bridge

dis - ci - ples of our Lord Je - sus Christ!

Discipleship

Bridge

Choir/All ... Soloist

Ne-ver too young { to preach the Gos - pel; / to feed the hun - gry; } ne-ver too young

{ to bring Good News! / to help the poor. } Ne-ver too young { to work for jus - tice; / to care for oth - ers. }

1 to Bridge

2 to Refrain We are

nev-er too young *to be God's Light!* Nev-er too young, nev-er too young!

*The entire Bridge may be sung by All.

I Will Bow and Be Simple

271

Cyprian Consiglio

A Cantor, All repeat

I will bow and be sim-ple, I will bow and be free. I will

bow and be sim-ple, yea, bow like a wil-low tree.

B Cantor, All repeat

I will bow and not be bro-ken, I will bear the eas-y yoke. Yes, I'll

bow, this is my to-ken, lean my back a-gainst the rock.

Note: Sing AA, BB, AA, BB, AA.

Discipleship

272

We Will Follow

Dan Brennan, Ken Canedo
and Jesse Manibusan

Refrain

You're the way, you're the truth, you're the life, we will fol-low; ev-'ry word, ev-'ry deed that we do. You're the way, you're the truth, you're the life, we will fol-low. Lead us, Lord, we will fol-low you.

Verses

1. In the hun-gry and the poor, those so eas-y to ig-nore.
2. In the strang-er on the street, those for-got-ten whom we meet.
3. In the hope-less ev-'ry-where, those who need some-one to care.

1. In the thirst-y and the weak, those who wan-der and in those who seek.
2. In the lone-ly far and near, those im-pris-oned, those who live in fear.
3. In the suf-f'ring through the land, those who long to touch God's heal-ing hand.

to Refrain

Discipleship

Alleluia! Raise the Gospel

Bernadette Farrell

Refrain

Al - le - lu - ia! Al - le - lu - ia! Raise the Gos - pel

o - ver the earth! Al - le - lu - ia! Al - le -

lu - ia! Peace and jus - tice bring-ing to birth!

Verses

1. Bless - ed those whose hearts are gen - tle. Bless - ed
2. Bless - ed those who work for jus - tice. Bless - ed
3. Trem - ble, you who build up rich - es. Trem - ble,
4. Trem - ble, you who thirst for pow - er. Trem - ble,
5. Glo - ry like the stars of heav - en— Glo - ry
6. Glo - ry to the Word of Jus - tice. Glo - ry

1. those whose spir - its are strong. Bless - ed those who
2. those who an - swer the call. Bless - ed those who
3. you with op - u - lent lives. Trem - ble, when you
4. you who live for ac - claim. Trem - ble, when you
5. like the sun in the sky— Glo - ry shines up -
6. to the Spir - it of Peace. Glo - ry to the

to Refrain

1. choose to bring forth right where there is wrong.
2. dare to dream of last - ing peace for all.
3. meet the poor and see Christ in their eyes.
4. find no com - fort in your wealth and fame.
5. on all peo - ple, e - qual in God's eyes.
6. God of Love whose bless - ings nev - er cease.

Freedom & Justice

274   Celebrate Freedom

Mark Friedman and Janet Vogt

Freedom & Justice

God of Abraham

Bernadette Farrell

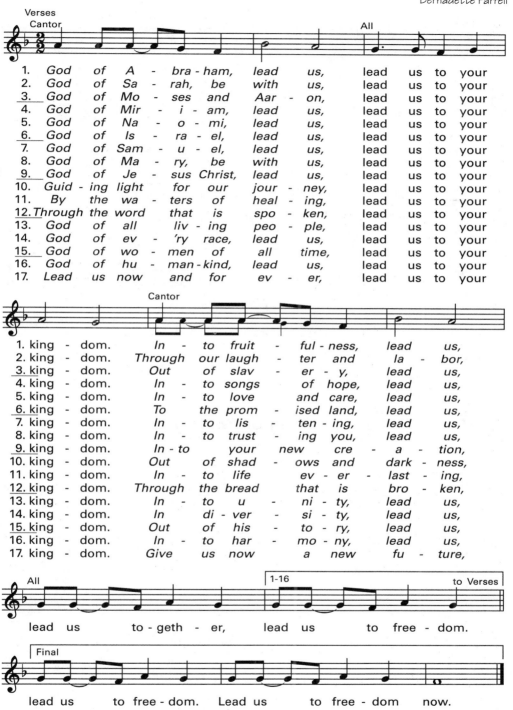

Freedom & Justice

276

Soon and Very Soon

SOON AND VERY SOON

1. Soon and ver - y soon, We are going to see the King;
2. No more cry-ing there, We are going to see the King;
3. No more dy-ing there, We are going to see the King;

1. Soon and ver - y soon, We are going to see the King;
2. No more cry-ing there, We are going to see the King;
3. No more dy-ing there, We are going to see the King;

1. Soon and ver - y soon, We are going to see the King; } Hal-le-
2. No more cry-ing there, We are going to see the King;
3. No more dy-ing there, We are going to see the King;

1-3. lu - jah! Hal-le - lu - jah! We're going to see the King.

Text: 57 57 57 86; Andraé Crouch. Music: Andraé Crouch; adapt. by William F. Smith. Text and music © 1976, Bud John Songs, Inc./Crouch Music. All rights reserved. Administered by EMI CMG Publishing. Used with permission.

277

Grant Us Peace

Ken Canedo

Refrain

Grant us peace, grant us peace.

On - ly love can make us free. Grant us peace.

Verses

1. Ev - er lov - ing God, hear our prayer. We, your chil -
2. Lead-ers of the world, hear God now. Beat the swords
3. Peo - ple of the world, we are one. May the na -

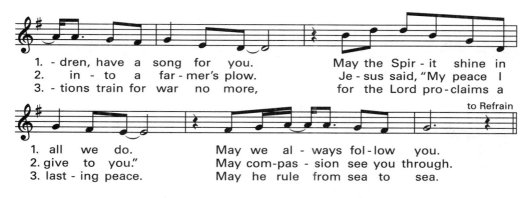

1. - dren, have a song for you.   May the Spir - it shine in
2. in - to a far - mer's plow.   Je - sus said, "My peace I
3. - tions train for war no more,   for the Lord pro - claims a

to Refrain

1. all we do.   May we al - ways fol - low you.
2. give to you."   May com - pas - sion see you through.
3. last - ing peace.   May he rule from sea to sea.

Text: Based on Micah 4:3; John 14:27; Psalm 85:9; Psalm 72:8. Text and music © 1994, 2006, Ken Canedo. Published by OCP. All rights reserved.

The Cry of the Poor 278

John Foley, S.J.

Refrain

The Lord hears the cry of the poor. Bless-ed be the Lord.

Verses: Slightly faster

1. I will bless the Lord at all times,   with praise
2. Let the low - ly hear and be glad: the Lord
3. Ev - 'ry spir - it crushed, God will save;   will be
4. We pro - claim your great - ness, O God,   your praise

1. ev - er in my mouth.   Let my soul glo - ry in the
2. lis - tens to their pleas;   and to hearts bro - ken, God is
3. ran - som for their lives;   will be safe shel - ter for their
4. ev - er in our mouth;   ev - 'ry face bright-ened in your

to Refrain

1. Lord, who will hear the cry of the poor.
2. near, who will hear the cry of the poor.
3. fears, and will hear the cry of the poor.
4. light, for you hear the cry of the poor.

Text: Based on Psalm 34:1–2, 17–18, 19, 22. Text and music © 1978, 1991, John Foley, S.J., and OCP. All rights reserved.

Freedom & Justice

279   The Lord Will Bless His People

Tom Booth

Text: Psalm 29:11, 1–2, 3–4, 9–10. Refrain text © 1969, 1981, ICEL. All rights reserved. Used with permission.
Verses © 1970, CCD. All rights reserved. Used with permission. Music © 1988, Tom Booth. Published by OCP. All rights reserved.

Freedom & Justice

We Shall Overcome

Traditional

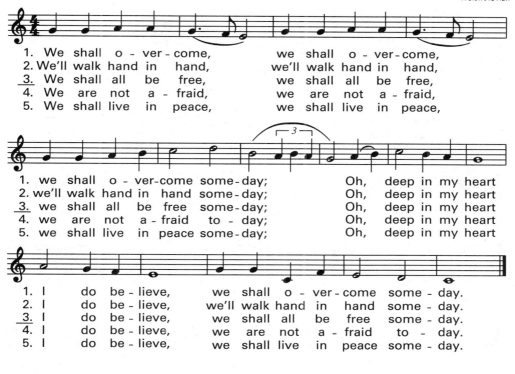

1. We shall o - ver - come, we shall o - ver - come,
2. We'll walk hand in hand, we'll walk hand in hand,
3. We shall all be free, we shall all be free,
4. We are not a - fraid, we are not a - fraid,
5. We shall live in peace, we shall live in peace,

1. we shall o - ver - come some - day; Oh, deep in my heart
2. we'll walk hand in hand some - day; Oh, deep in my heart
3. we shall all be free some - day; Oh, deep in my heart
4. we are not a - fraid to - day; Oh, deep in my heart
5. we shall live in peace some - day; Oh, deep in my heart

1. I do be - lieve, we shall o - ver - come some - day.
2. I do be - lieve, we'll walk hand in hand some - day.
3. I do be - lieve, we shall all be free some - day.
4. I do be - lieve, we are not a - fraid to - day.
5. I do be - lieve, we shall live in peace some - day.

Freedom & Justice

281

Faces of Our Friends

Sarah Hart and Celia Whitler

Verses

1. I don't think that you're a God we can-not see, just a
2. I know there are man - y souls we have not met. There's a

1. pres-ence in the sky, on - ly a mys - ter-y.
2. world of hearts in need who do not know you yet; but

1. I be-lieve there's more to you than meets the eye. And I
2. I be-lieve that love a-lone can speak to them. So if there's

1. see a lit - tle more of you as time goes by.
2. one thing we can be in life, let us be a friend.

Refrain

'Cause in the fac-es of our friends you are ob - vi-ous. In the

fac-es of our friends you are clear. And through the hearts of those we

1

love, you reach for us; in the fac-es of our friends you are here.

3 to Verse 2 **2**

fac - es of our friends you are

Bridge **14** **3**

here. In the fac-es of our

Final

friends you are here. fac-es of our friends you are here.

Retreats

I See You

Rich Mullins

Verses

1. Lord, you're lead - ing me with a cloud by day,
2. And you take my hand and you wash it clean.
3. And the ea - gle flies and the riv - ers run.
4. Well, the grass will die and the flow - ers fall,

1. and then __ in the night, the glow __ of a
2. I know the prom - ised land is light - years a -
3. I look __ through the night and I can see the
4. but your __ Word's a - live and will __ be __

Refrain

1. burn - ing flame. And ev - 'ry - where I go I see you.
2. head of me.
3. ris - ing sun.
4. af - ter all.

[1] to Verse 2

Ev - 'ry - where I go I see you.

[2-4]

And ev - 'ry - where I go I see you. Ev - 'ry -

[1] to Verse 3 [2] **2** to Verse 4

where I go I see you.

Final

And ev - 'ry - where I go I see you. Ev - 'ry -

where I go I see you. And ev - 'ry - where I go I see

you. Ev - 'ry - where I go I see you.

283 Lean on Me

Bill Withers

1. Some - times in our lives   we all have pain,
2. Please   swal-low your pride   if I have things
3. If   there is a load   you have to bear

1. we all have sor - row.   But   if we are wise
2. you need to bor - row,   for   no one can fill
3. that you can't car - ry,   I'm   right up the road.

1. we know that there's   al - ways to - mor - row.
2. those of your needs   that you won't let   show.
3. I'll share your load   if you just call   me.

Refrain

Lean on me   when you're not strong   and I'll be your friend.

I'll help you car - ry on,   for   it won't be long

1   to Verse 2

till I'm gon-na need   some-bod-y to lean   on.

2, 3   **Bridge**

on.   You just call on me, broth-er, when you need a hand.

We all need some-bod-y to lean   on.   I just

might have a prob - lem   that you'll un - der-stand.   We all

need some-bod-y to lean on. on. Just

call me, (when you need a friend,) call me,

(in the morn-ing,) call me, (when you need a friend,)

call me, (in the eve-ning,) call me.

This Little Light of Mine

284

Spiritual

1. This lit - tle light of mine,   I'm gon-na let it shine.
2. Ev - 'ry - where I go,   I'm gon-na let it shine.
3. Je - sus gave it to me;   I'm gon-na let it shine.

1. This lit - tle light of mine,   I'm gon-na let it shine.
2. Ev - 'ry - where I go,   I'm gon-na let it shine.
3. Je - sus gave it to me;   I'm gon-na let it shine.

1. This lit - tle light of mine,
2. Ev - 'ry - where I go,   I'm gon-na let it shine.
3. Je - sus gave it to me;

1-3. Let it shine, let it shine, let it shine.

285

Keep Me in Your Heart

Janèt Sullivan Whitaker

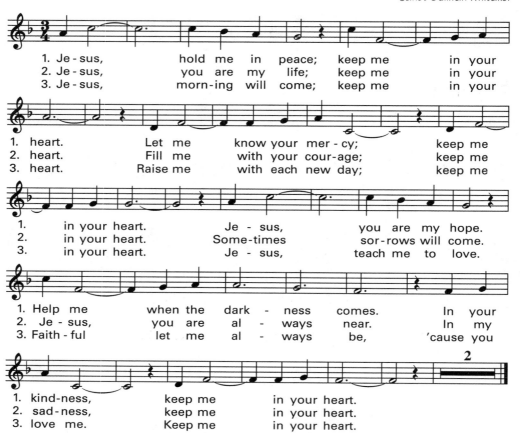

1. Je-sus, hold me in peace; keep me in your
2. Je-sus, you are my life; keep me in your
3. Je-sus, morn-ing will come; keep me in your

1. heart. Let me know your mer-cy; keep me
2. heart. Fill me with your cour-age; keep me
3. heart. Raise me with each new day; keep me

1. in your heart. Je-sus, you are my hope.
2. in your heart. Some-times sor-rows will come.
3. in your heart. Je-sus, teach me to love.

1. Help me when the dark - ness comes. In your
2. Je - sus, you are al - ways near. In my
3. Faith - ful let me al - ways be, 'cause you

1. kind-ness, keep me in your heart.
2. sad-ness, keep me in your heart.
3. love me. Keep me in your heart.

Mountain of God

286

Marc Cavallero, Dan Brennan
and Ken Canedo

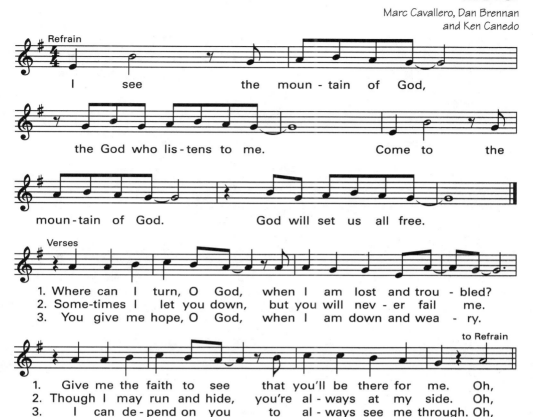

Refrain

I see the moun-tain of God, the God who lis-tens to me. Come to the moun-tain of God. God will set us all free.

Verses

1. Where can I turn, O God, when I am lost and trou-bled?
2. Some-times I let you down, but you will nev-er fail me.
3. You give me hope, O God, when I am down and wea-ry.

to Refrain

1. Give me the faith to see that you'll be there for me. Oh,
2. Though I may run and hide, you're al-ways at my side. Oh,
3. I can de-pend on you to al-ways see me through. Oh,

Text: Based on Psalm 121. Text and music © 1998, Marc Cavallero, Dan Brennan and Ken Canedo.
Published by spiritandsong.com®, a division of OCP. All rights reserved.

Retreats

287   We Are the Light

Jesse Manibusan

Refrain

We are the light, light of the world shin-ing for the world to see! We are the light, light of the world shin-ing for the world to see!

Verses

1. Dark-ness grow-ing ev-'ry-where, hid-ing in the light!
2. Some-one calls us each by name, know-ing our dis-guise,
3. Lis-ten to that still, small voice call-ing us to life,

1. How can our hope en-dure this end-less night?
2. to hear and act in faith, to re-al-ize that
3. to make a con-scious choice to live in Christ.

to Refrain

BUG MUSIC – HOLLYWOOD
Pants Down Music
7750 Sunset Blvd
Los Angeles, CA 90046
(323) 969-0988
Fax (323) 969-0968

COMISIÓN EPISCOPAL ESPAÑOLA DE LITURGIA
Añastro, 1
28033 Madrid,
Spain

CONFRATERNITY OF CHRISTIAN DOCTRINE, INC. (CCD)
3211 4th Street NE
Washington, DC 20017

DOG NOT INCLUDED (ASCAP)
P.O. Box 1385
Franklin, TN 37065
www.celiamusic.net

EMI CMG PUBLISHING
Birdwing Music/BMG Songs, Inc.
Bud John Songs
Crouch Music
Curious? Music U.K.
Meadowgreen Music Company
Meaux Mercy
Mountain Spring Music
Six Steps Music
Storm Boy Music
Straightway Music
Thankyou Music
worshiptogether.com songs
P.O. Box 5084
Brentwood, TN 37024-5084
(615) 371-4300

HAL LEONARD CORPORATION
Interior Music
7777 W. Bluemound Road
Milwaukee, WI 53213
(414) 774-3630
Fax (414) 774-3259

HEARTBEAT MUSIC/ AUGUST MUSIC
P.O. Box 20
Donnellson, IA 52625

HOPE PUBLISHING CO.
Stainer & Bell, Ltd.
380 S. Main Place
Carol Stream, IL 60188
(800) 323-1049

INTEGRITY MEDIA, INC.
Integrity's Hosanna! Music
c/o Hal Leonard Corporation
7777 W. Bluemound Road
Milwaukee, WI 53213
(414) 774-3630
Fax (414) 774-3259

INTERNATIONAL COMMITTEE ON ENGLISH IN THE LITURGY (ICEL)
1522 K Street NW, Suite 1000
Washington, DC 20005-1202
(202) 347-0800 Ext. 2
Fax (202) 347-1839

LENSONGS PUBLISHING, INC. (ASCAP)
800 County Road 27
Florence, AL 35634-2881

LORENZ CORPORATION
501 E. 3rd St.
Dayton, OH 45401
(800) 444-1144 Ext. 1

MPCA (MUSIC PUBLISHING COMPANY OF AMERICA), LLC
MPCA Lehsem Songs
c/o Hal Leonard Corporation
7777 W. Bluemound Road
Milwaukee, WI 53213
(414) 774-3630
Fax (414) 774-3259

MUSIC SERVICES, INC.
BMG Songs, Inc.
Brentwood-Benson Music Publishing, Inc.
Careers—BMG Music Publishing
Kid Brothers of St. Frank
Make Way Music
Maranatha! Music
Maranatha Praise, Inc.
Mercy/Vineyard Publishing
New Spring, a division of Zomba Enterprises, Inc.
Vineyard Songs (Canada)
Vineyard Songs (UK/EIRE)
White Plastic Bag Music
1526 Otter Creek Road
Nashville, TN 37215

MZS ENTERTAINMENT LLC
Sunday Best Music
PO Box 896
La Vergne, TN 37086
(615) 477-8928

OXFORD UNIVERSITY PRESS
198 Madison Avenue
New York, NY 10016-4314
(212) 726-6000
Fax (212) 726-6441

SIMPLEVILLE MUSIC (ASCAP)
P.O. Box 40307
Nashville, TN 37204-0307
(615) 250-2452
Fax (615) 346-9616

SONY/ATV MUSIC PUBLISHING
Sony/ATV Songs LLC
c/o Hall Leonard Corporation
7777 W. Bluemound Road
Milwaukee, WI 53213
(414) 774-3630
Fax (414) 774-3259

**VERNACULAR HYMNS
PUBLISHING CO.**
8604 Summer Creek Rd.
Bakersfield, CA 93311

WALTON MUSIC CORPORATION
Utryck, Sweden
c/o Louann Cassano
1 Rebecca Court
Randolph, NJ 07869
(973) 743-6444

WORD MUSIC, LLC
Liturgy Legacy Music
c/o Opryland Music Group
PO Box 128469
Nashville, TN 37212

HEALING
*See also Liturgical Index: Rites of
the Church, Rite of Anointing
(Care of the Sick)*
- 82 Able
- 132 Because the Lord Is
My Shepherd
- 7 Bless the Lord
- 64 Bread for the World
- 9 City of God
- 241 Come to the River
- 67 Come to the Water
- 91 Great God
- 175 Healing Hands
- 92 Here I Am (Booth)
- 97 I Could Sing of Your Love Forever
- 179 I Thirst
- 227 Jesus Is with Us
- 119 Jesus, I Trust in You
- 20 Lead Us to the Water:
Gathering
- 27 On Eagle's Wings
- 56 The Lord Is Kind and Merciful
(Modlin)
- 186 Transfigure Us, O Lord

HEAVEN
See Eternal Life/Heaven

HOLY NAME
- 4 Alleluia! Sing to Jesus
- 5 At the Name of Jesus
- 7 Bless the Lord
- 94 He Is Exalted
- 201 Holy Is His Name
- 99 I Will Lift Up Your Name
- 23 Lift Up Your Hearts
- 101 Lord, I Lift Your Name on High
- 73 One Bread, One Cup
- 56 The Lord Is Kind and Merciful
(Modlin)

HOLY ORDERS
*See Liturgical Index:
Rites of the Church, Holy Orders*

HOLY SPIRIT
- 236 Adoration
- 3 Alleluia! Give the Glory
- 86 Be Lifted High
- 192 Come, Holy Ghost
- 230 Come, Holy Spirit
- 166 Cry the Gospel
- 231 Envía Tu Espíritu
- 114 Father, I Adore You
- 232 God Is Calling Your Name
- 233 Holy Spirit
- 189 Holy Spirit, Come Now
- 21 Let the River Flow
- 57 Lord, Send Out Your Spirit
- 196 Now Is the Time
- 243 Sacred Silence
- 105 Shine, Jesus, Shine
- 199 Spirit, Come Down
- 256 The Call
- 168 They'll Know We Are Christians

HOLY TRINITY
*See Liturgical Index: Solemnities
of the Lord in Ordinary Time,
The Most Holy Trinity*

HOMELESSNESS
*See Global Family, Justice,
Social Concern*

HOPE
See also Faith, Trust
- 214 Amazing Grace
- 213 Be Not Afraid
- 8 Christ, Be Our Light
- 9 City of God
- 66 Come to the Lord
- 67 Come to the Water
- 125 Enter the Journey/
Sigue el Camino
- 13 Glory Bound
- 116 How Can I Keep from Singing
- 282 I See You
- 115 I Shall Not Want
- 246 I Will Have Faith in You
- 134 In Every Age
- 248 Jacob's Ladder
- 22 Let Us Come to Be One Body
- 286 Mountain of God
- 120 My Soul Is Thirsting/
As Morning Breaks
- 27 On Eagle's Wings
- 25 Rain Down
- 142 Thank You, God
- 278 The Cry of the Poor
- 42 The Lord Is My Shepherd
- 123 To You, O God, I Lift Up My Soul
- 153 Waiting in Silence
- 212 Walk On with Jesus
- 167 We Are God's Work of Art
- 287 We Are the Light
- 36 We Gotta Love
- 280 We Shall Overcome
- 143 With All Our Hearts

HOSPITALITY
See Welcome

HOUSE OF GOD
*See Liturgical Index: Rites of the
Church, Dedication of a Church*

HUMILITY
- 209 Father, I Give Myself
- 201 Holy Is His Name
- 283 Lean on Me
- 278 The Cry of the Poor
- 43 To You, O Lord
- 35 We Are the Light of the World

HUNGER
- 64 Bread for the World
- 69 Feed Us, Lord
- 68 Here at This Table
- 18 In This Place
- 75 Table of Plenty
- 80 Ven al Banquete/
Come to the Feast
- 212 Walk On with Jesus

ILLNESS
*See Liturgical Index: Rites of
the Church, Rite of Anointing
(Care of the Sick)*

JESUS CHRIST
*See Good Shepherd, Holy Name;
Liturgical Index: Solemnities of
the Lord in Ordinary Time*

JOURNEY
- 214 Amazing Grace
- 213 Be Not Afraid
- 9 City of God
- 125 Enter the Journey/
Sigue el Camino
- 217 Fly Like a Bird

- 275 God of Abraham
- 261 I Will Choose Christ
- 248 Jacob's Ladder
- 19 Lead Me, Lord
- 129 Pescador de Hombres/
Lord, You Have Come
- 276 Soon and Very Soon
- 256 The Call
- 186 Transfigure Us, O Lord
- 212 Walk On with Jesus
- 37 We Are Marching/Siyahamba
- 280 We Shall Overcome
- 235 You Have Called Us

JOY
- 1 All the Ends of the Earth
- 9 City of God
- 139 For the Beauty of the Earth
- 13 Glory Bound
- 140 Grateful
- 97 I Could Sing of Your Love Forever
- 59 I Rejoiced
- 99 I Will Lift Up Your Name
- 49 Let All the Earth Cry Out
- 23 Lift Up Your Hearts
- 195 Nadie en el Sepulcro/
No One in the Tomb
- 157 Praise Him with Cymbals
- 28 Sing Alleluia
- 142 Thank You, God
- 107 The Lord Has Done Great Things
- 58 This Is the Day
- 34 Venimos/We Come
- 111 We Ever Will Praise You

JUBILATION
See Joy, Praise

JUBILEE/HOLY YEAR/MILLENNIUM
*See Liturgical Index:
Rites of the Church, Holy Orders,
Rite of Religious Profession*

JUSTICE
- 273 Alleluia! Raise the Gospel
- 87 Bless the Lord
- 274 Celebrate Freedom
- 9 City of God
- 231 Envía Tu Espíritu
- 127 God Has Chosen Me
- 228 Jesus, You Are Bread for Us
- 50 Lord, Every Nation
- 51 Lord, Show Us Your Mercy
and Love
- 31 Somos el Cuerpo de Cristo/
We Are the Body of Christ
- 78 Taste and See
- 278 The Cry of the Poor
- 80 Ven al Banquete/
Come to the Feast
- 34 Venimos/We Come
- 35 We Are the Light of the World
- 280 We Shall Overcome
- 38 With One Voice

KINGDOM/REIGN OF GOD
*See also Liturgical Index:
Solemnities of the Lord in Ordinary Time,
Our Lord Jesus Christ the King*
- 177 Above All
- 4 Alleluia! Sing to Jesus
- 5 At the Name of Jesus
- 85 Awesome God
- 9 City of God
- 45 God Mounts His Throne
- 275 God of Abraham

11 Give God the Glory
275 God of Abraham
201 Holy Is His Name
263 Light of the World
101 Lord, I Lift Your Name on High
155 Love Has Come
73 One Bread, One Cup
197 Rise Up with Him
137 Saints of God
198 Song of the Cross
222 Sweet Redeemer
184 The King of Glory
46 The Lord Is My Light
and My Salvation
58 This Is the Day
187 What Wondrous Love Is This
200 Worthy Is the Lamb
39 You Are the Way

SEARCHING/SEEKING
See Longing for God

SECOND COMING
See also Kingdom/Reign of God;
Liturgical Index: The Liturgical Year,
Season of Advent
5 At the Name of Jesus
150 Find Us Ready
96 I Can Only Imagine
276 Soon and Very Soon
200 Worthy Is the Lamb

SELF-ESTEEM
See Love of God for Us

SENDING FORTH
See also Discipleship, Ministry/Mission
83 Alabaré
213 Be Not Afraid
9 City of God
166 Cry the Gospel
150 Find Us Ready
259 Go Light Your World
260 Go Make a Difference
12 Go Ye Out
127 God Has Chosen Me
14 God, Creator, God Most High
264 Here I Am, Lord
26 Malo! Malo! Thanks Be to God
77 The Eyes and Hands of Christ
284 This Little Light of Mine
37 We Are Marching/Siyahamba
287 We Are the Light
35 We Are the Light of the World
36 We Gotta Love
38 With One Voice
265 Witnesses

SERENITY
See Confidence, Faith,
Love of God for Us, Trust

SERVICE
See Commissioning, Discipleship,
Ministry/Mission, Social Concern

SHEPHERD
See Good Shepherd

SICKNESS
See Healing; Liturgical Index:
Rites of the Church, Rite of Anointing
(Care of the Sick)

SIN
47 Be Merciful, O Lord
221 Nothing Is Beyond You
182 Purify My Heart
137 Saints of God
222 Sweet Redeemer
223 The Lord Is Kind and Merciful
(Booth)
56 The Lord Is Kind and Merciful
(Modlin)
43 To You, O Lord
167 We Are God's Work of Art
240 You Alone

SOCIAL CONCERN
273 Alleluia! Raise the Gospel
87 Bless the Lord
64 Bread for the World
274 Celebrate Freedom
8 Christ, Be Our Light
9 City of God
67 Come to the Water
231 Envía Tu Espíritu
69 Feed Us, Lord
10 Gather Your People
259 Go Light Your World
127 God Has Chosen Me
16 In This Holy Place
228 Jesus, You Are Bread for Us
270 Never Too Young
74 Pan de Vida
31 Somos el Cuerpo de Cristo/
We Are the Body of Christ
32 Tell It Out
278 The Cry of the Poor
80 Ven al Banquete/
Come to the Feast
34 Venimos/We Come
79 We Are One Body
35 We Are the Light of the World
280 We Shall Overcome
272 We Will Follow
38 With One Voice

SOLIDARITY
See Justice, Social Concern, Unity

SORROW
See Comfort, Lament

SPANISH LANGUAGE
See Bilingual/Multilingual

SPIRITUAL GIFTS
See Holy Spirit; Liturgical Index:
Rites of the Church, Confirmation

STEWARDSHIP
8 Christ, Be Our Light
231 Envía Tu Espíritu
139 For the Beauty of the Earth
141 Sacred Creation
278 The Cry of the Poor
35 We Are the Light of the World

SUFFERING
See also Global Family, Justice,
Social Concern
66 Come to the Lord
67 Come to the Water
220 Jesus, My Everything
41 My God, My God
280 We Shall Overcome

SUFFERING OF CHRIST
177 Above All
176 From a King to a King
178 In the Silence of the Garden
32 Tell It Out
212 Walk On with Jesus
188 Your Only Son

SUNDAY, THE LORD'S DAY
58 This Is the Day

THANKSGIVING
139 For the Beauty of the Earth
90 Forever
210 Friends for Life
61 God's Love Is Everlasting
140 Grateful
99 I Will Lift Up Your Name
53 If Today
26 Malo! Malo! Thanks Be to God
142 Thank You, God
143 With All Our Hearts

THIRST
See also Longing for God
64 Bread for the World
67 Come to the Water
68 Here at This Table
48 My Soul Is Thirsting for You
120 My Soul Is Thirsting/
As Morning Breaks
80 Ven al Banquete/
Come to the Feast

TRANSFIGURATION
See Liturgical Index: Solemnities and
Feasts, The Transfiguration of the Lord

TRIDUUM
See Liturgical Index: The Liturgical Year,
Easter Triduum

TRINITY
See Liturgical Index: Solemnities
of the Lord in Ordinary Time,
The Most Holy Trinity

TRUST
See also Faith, Hope
213 Be Not Afraid
209 Father, I Give Myself
91 Great God
92 Here I Am (Booth)
266 Hey, You, Stand Up for God
116 How Can I Keep from Singing
115 I Shall Not Want
246 I Will Have Faith in You
248 Jacob's Ladder
118 Jesus, Come to Us
119 Jesus, I Trust in You
249 Jump in the Water
283 Lean on Me
121 Lord of All Hopefulness
221 Nothing Is Beyond You
27 On Eagle's Wings
25 Rain Down
124 See, I Make All Things New
253 Shepherd Song
183 Show Us Your Mercy
142 Thank You, God
33 The King of Love My Shepherd Is
42 The Lord Is My Shepherd
117 Thy Word Is a Lamp
153 Waiting in Silence
60 With the Lord There Is Mercy